Contents

What are the characteristics of Britain's landscapes?

The **United Kingdom** (UK) shares the **British Isles** with the **Republic of Ireland**. These islands were famously described by William Shakespeare as a "**precious stone set in the silver sea.**" It is not hard to see why. Britain has a diverse array of beautiful and dramatic landscapes, from towering mountains to rolling hills and flat plains.

Our coastline, **over 11,000 miles** long, contains wild stretches of long sandy beaches, dramatic cliffs, sheltered coves and muddy estuaries. These landscapes have developed as the result of a complex **interaction between geology, climate, vegetation and the geomorphic processes** associated with rivers and glaciers. Increasingly, over the last three thousand years, **human beings have played a crucial role in shaping the** landscapes and apes which we take for granted today.

The geological history of the British Isles has led to the formation of **distinct areas of highlands and lowlands.** Mountain ranges are found to the north and west while the land becomes lower and flatter in the east. These mountain rages ranges have affected the climate, with the **north and west receiving significantly more rainfall than the south east.**

In turn, the relief of the land and the associated climate have determined how humans beings have used the land for farming. The uplands of Snowdonia, the Lake District and Pennines have become famous for their **hill sheep farming,** whilst the gently undulating and flat lands of Lincolnshire and East Anglia have become the **'breadbasket of England'** – growing a wide variety of crops on their rich and fertile soils.

The far north of Scotland is graced by the dramatic mountains and moors of **Sutherland,** described as the 'last great wilderness in Britain.' Sutherland is one of the most remote, sparsely populated and least visited areas of Britain.

Meanwhile, the Yorkshire Dales and Peak District National Parks, at the southern ···

While only a small percentage of our landscapes are urban, almost all of the UK has been altered by human activity. As a result nearly all our landscapes are the product of both physical and human processes.

▲ fig.1 **Ardvreck Castle, Sutherland**

▲ fig.2 **Gordale Scar, The Yorkshire Dales**

▲ fig.3 **Whitby Abbey, North Yorkshire**

▲fig.4 **The Norfolk Broads**

N

Land under 200m

▼fig.7 **Mountains of Mourne**

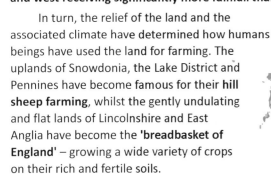

▼ fig.6 **Grimspond, Dartmoor** F

fig.5 **The South Downs** ▼

100km

The physical landscapes of the UK have distinctive characteristics.

UK geology and climate

The **geology** of Britain is diverse and complex. To simplify things it is often customary to divide the country into two zones with a line drawn from **Exmouth**, on the Dorset coast, to the mouth of the **River Tees** at Hartlepool. The **Tees-Exe line** neatly divides the uplands of ✳ the north and west from the lowlands of the south and east. *see next page*

North of the Tees-Exe line the geology is dominated by older and **more resistant rocks**, such as carboniferous limestone, or igneous rocks such a granite or metamorphic schists. These rocks are more resistant to erosion. They have been worn down more slowly to leave **hills and mountain ranges.**

In the lowlands the climate is significantly drier than the mountainous west and north. This is because there is less **relief rainfall**. The average annual rainfall for Norwich, in low-lying East Anglia, is just 674mm.

In contrast, the village of Capel Curig in the Snowdonia National Park receives 2612mm annually. Temperatures are higher in the lowlands: not only are they mostly further south but also they do not experience the cooling of air experienced with a gain in altitude. As a general rule, temperatures fall by 1°C for every 100m gained in height. Norwich, with an approximate altitude of 36m, has an average summer high of 21.5°C. However, in winter, temperatures may fall to an average low of 1.3°C when cold polar winds blow from northern Europe and the arctic over a **cold North Sea.**

Hot summer temperatures can result in the rapid warming of the land surface. As a result, air above the land is warmed and expands, rising quickly into the atmosphere. As it rises the air cools producing **cumulonimbus** thunderclouds, resulting in short but heavy downpours of **convectional rain.**

Climate, soil and vegetation

Climate and geology combine to create soil. **Soil creation is a slow process** which has happened in most of Britain in the last 10,000 years, after the ice sheets melted.

▲ fig.8 **Woodland covered England**

Soils tend to be **thinner on high mountain slopes** but **thicker and more fertile on the valley floors** and lowlands. In the warmer temperatures of the lowlands, plant growth is faster and biological activity more effective creating soils.

Most of Britain used to be covered in thick forests. The leaves shed each winter by deciduous trees, such as oak, ash and beech, have been integrated by earthworms, fungi and bacteria into rich, **acid brown earths**.

Further north in colder climates, coniferous trees such as Scots Pine dominate the forests. Pine needles do not break down as easily as leaves. Here highly-acidic **podsols** form. These are less productive for agriculture and produce **poor quality grazing for livestock**.

In areas such as the chalk South Downs or limestone Yorkshire Dales, the rock chemically weathers to produce a thin but fertile soil called a **rendzina**. This soil is too thin for growing crops but excellent for growing grass. So in these areas pastoral farming has flourished, with sheep grazing the higher ground and cattle in the lower valleys.

The geology of the British Isles

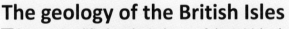

▼ fig.9: **A simplified geological map of the British Isles**

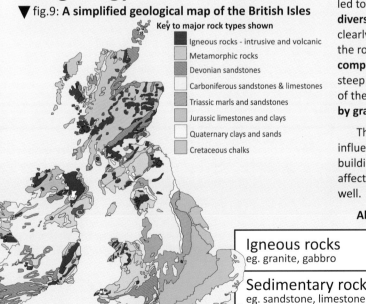

Key to major rock types shown
- Igneous rocks - intrusive and volcanic
- Metamorphic rocks
- Devonian sandstones
- Carboniferous sandstones & limestones
- Triassic marls and sandstones
- Jurassic limestones and clays
- Quaternary clays and sands
- Cretaceous chalks

The geology of the UK has led to the creation of its **diverse landscapes.** This can be clearly seen when comparing the rolling **South Downs, composed of chalk**, to the steep and dramatic mountains of the **Cairngorms, dominated by granite.**

The local rock type has also influenced the choice of local building materials - and so has affected our built landscapes as well.

Aberdeen is known as the ↗

'**granite city**' as many of its buildings are made from the local granite. Much of the older housing of the Pennine mill towns is made of tough **sedimentary millstone grit.**

In the south and east of England **brick was favoured because of large clay deposits.** However, London's impressive public buildings are mostly constructed from Portland limestone from the Isle of Purbeck.

Meanwhile, **Welsh slate** was used to tile the roofs of millions of houses across the entire country.

Igneous rocks eg. granite, gabbro	Formed from the cooling of molten minerals to create extrusive (surface) or intrusive (underground) rocks.	Common in Scottish Highlands but also outcrops in areas such as Cornwall and Snowdonia.
Sedimentary rocks eg. sandstone, limestone	Formed from compaction and cementation of particles of eroded rock or organic materials such as shells.	Most common rock type in UK. Rocks tend to become older further north.
Metamorphic rocks eg. gneiss, slate	Formed by heat and pressure, often close to volcanic activity, altering the structure of existing rocks.	Most common in Scotland and areas of volcanic activity such as with Welsh slate.

What are the characteristics of Britain's lowlands?

Most of Britain's lowlands are found **east of the Tees-Exe line**. The lowlands are also where most of Britain's major cities are found. These low lying areas, below 200m above sea level, are close to rivers and **flat, productive land** for arable farming. They were perfect locations for the villages, which grew into towns and then into cities.

London, with its population of 8.5 million people, is located on the **river terraces either side of the River Thames**.

Further north, the Vale of York is a wide expanse of flat land between the Pennines and North York Moors. The geology has produced **fertile soils** which

fig.10 **Drax power station**

make the area rich in agricultural land. This area had already been cleared of most woodland for farming before the Roman invasion, 2000 years ago.

During the 20th Century the underlying **coal measures made the Vale**

of York a rich coal field. Power stations such as the massive **Drax** station, opened in 1974, were built to burn the coal. In the era of global warming Drax is being **converted to run on bio-fuels**. ✳ look up

The flat land makes an **ideal transport corridor** for the A1 and A19 roads and the East Coast Mainline railway. However, the flat land makes the area susceptible to river flooding, as with York's **River Fosse**.

The soft, **drift geology** of these areas makes the coastline susceptible to erosion. On Yorkshire's **Holderness coast** an average of 1.5 metres, or 2 millions tonnes, is eroded annually from the clay cliffs.

Arable farming

Overlying the solid geology, the so-called **country rock**, of the lowlands is often a deep layer of **river sediments** or **glacial deposits** called **drift**. These layers of weathered rock have produced deep, rich and **fertile soils**. They were once covered in dense woodland for thousands of years before being cleared for farming.

These rich soils have led to the development of highly productive **arable farms** in the lowlands. The warm summers, alongside the soils, have created an ideal landscape for arable farming. The **growing of crops**, from cereals to oil seed, dominates the landscape of the lowland countryside. Many of the farms in Lincolnshire and Norfolk grow **vegetables**. They are sold **fresh**, **frozen** or **tinned**.

Not all arable farming takes place south of the Tees-Exe line. There are other similar areas of rich fertile soils such as the **Lancashire** and **Cheshire plains**, or the gently rolling hills of **Perthshire**.

▼ fig.11 **The relief of the British Isles**

N

Tees- Exe Line

Cromer

Liscombe

100km

Brighton

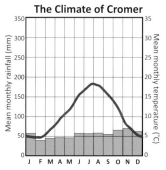

Thinking it through Compare and contrast the **rainfall figures for Liscombe** in the south-west with **Brighton and Cromer** on the south and east coasts. (4)

The Climate of Liscombe

Mean monthly rainfall (mm) / Mean monthly temperature (°C)

J F M A M J J A S O N D

The Climate of Brighton

Mean monthly rainfall (mm) / Mean monthly temperature (°C)

J F M A M J J A S O N D

The Climate of Cromer

Mean monthly rainfall (mm) / Mean monthly temperature (°C)

J F M A M J J A S O N D

What are the landscape features of Britian's lowlands?

To the south of the Tees-Exe line are **younger, often sedimentary, rocks.** These help create the landscapes typical of the lowlands. While described as lowlands, not all the land is flat. **Clay vales are flat areas of land smoothed by rivers** flowing over the clay. They are bordered by **steeper and higher chalk escarpments** such as the North and South Downs.

These **escarpments are gentle, low-lying hills** rather than mountain ranges. They were formed as a result of the folding and buckling of the land caused by the building of the Alps in southern Europe. This formed **synclines and anticlines** (folds) in the rock strata. After erosion of the surface layers, the **more resistant chalk** escarpment was left standing higher than the softer clay.

fig.12 **The South Downs and clay vale to the north.**

fig.13 **Barton Broad, Norfolk**

The **most fertile soils in the UK** are found in the flat **fenland** of Lincolnshire and Cambridgeshire. These soils are rich **loams** reclaimed from the sea. To the east, in Norfolk, much of the area is covered with **glacial till** deposited by ice sheets. In some places the drift has been bulldozed by the ice into high ridges to form cliffs such as the **Cromer Ridge**. These cliffs are easily eroded. In places along the coast, such as at West Runton, the sea has exposed the **underlying chalk**.

The most famous 'natural' landscape feature of Norfolk are the sixty three shallow lakes called **broads**. They are, in fact, not natural at all. The broads were **medieval peat workings**. They began to flood as sea levels rose. This created a network of lakes, connected by seven rivers, flowing into the North Sea.

Thinking it through

1. Using Fig.9 on page 5, describe the distribution of **igneous rocks** in the British Isles. (3)

2. Using figure 11 on page 6, describe the distribution of **lowland areas** within the British isles. (4)

3. With reference to the geology map of the British Isles (fig.9, page 5) **suggest reasons for the distribution of lowland areas** in the United Kingdom. (4)

4. With reference to relief, explain why the **south-east of England receives less rainfall than north Wales.** (4)

Rural or urban landscapes?

It is very hard to find many places in the British Isles that do not show signs of human influence. Eighty percent of the British population live in **urban areas - town and cities**. So you could be forgiven for thinking that most of our landscapes are urban ones.

However, there is some debate about w**hat constitutes an urban landscape?** Is it just the built on area or does it include the parks and gardens of our cities, or indeed the market gardens (small farms) and equestrian land (fields for horses) often found on the **urban fringe**?

A study by the **Office of National Statistics** found that 6.8% of the UK was urban - a figure which actually included most villages and rural roads. The urban landscape accounts for 10.6% of England, 1.9% of Scotland, 3.6% of Northern Ireland and 4.1% of Wales. That means almost 93% is rural.

On top of this, **54% of towns and cities are actually green spaces** such as parks, allotments and sports pitches. Furthermore, domestic **gardens account for another 18%** of urban land use; rivers, canals, lakes and reservoirs an additional 6.6%. So the actual area of land built on in the UK is about **2.3%.**

Just because an area isn't built on doesn't mean it is free of human influence. That is why many people support the concept of **'re-wilding'** some of our countryside: reducing human influence and reintroducing lost species such as beavers and lynx.

KEY TERMS

Arable farming: the growing of crops, such as wheat or potatoes, on the land.

Chalk escarpment: the ridge of higher ground of chalk (cretaceous limestone) with a steep scarp slope and gentle dip slope.

Clay vale: flat or gently undulating area of land overlying sedimentary clays.

Commercial agriculture: the growing of crops or the raising of animals for sale.

Country rock: the rock type typical of an area, sometimes called basement rock.

Pastoral farming: the raising of animals for meat, eggs, milk, wool or a combination of products.

The physical landscapes of the UK have distinctive characteristics.

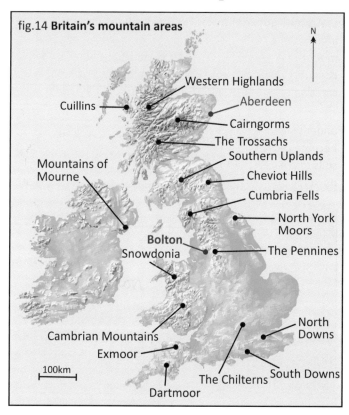

What are the characteristics of Britain's uplands?

There are many types of **upland areas** within the British Isles, from the granite landscapes of **Dartmoor** in the south west of England to the granite mountains of the Scottish **Cairngorms**. The **Pennines** create a ridge of limestone and gritstone hills running down the backbone of England, from the Scottish borders to the Midlands. Some upland areas have been affected by glaciation while others, such as **Dartmoor**, have escaped the effect of ice.

In the north and west, the rocks tend to be more resistant, resulting in hills and mountains. This has affected the climate. Warm, moisture-laden air flowing in from the Atlantic is forced to rise over the higher ground. As it rises it cools and the water vapour condenses to form clouds which deliver their **relief rainfall** over the western hills.

As the air descends on the other side of the hills it warms again. Remaining moisture tends to evaporate, resulting in much drier weather on the lee side of the hills. This **rain shadow** explains the difference between the annual rainfall in Bolton and York. Bolton, on the windward side of the Pennines gets 1120mm of rain while York, further east receives just 626mm of rainfall each year.

The landscapes of the uplands have also been **shaped by agriculture and industry.** The high rainfall and shallow soils of the hills have made the area ideal for **pastoral sheep farming.**

fig.14 **Britain's mountain areas**

Cuillins · Western Highlands · Aberdeen · Cairngorms · The Trossachs · Southern Uplands · Cheviot Hills · Cumbria Fells · North York Moors · The Pennines · Mountains of Mourne · Bolton · Snowdonia · Snowdonia · Cambrian Mountains · Exmoor · North Downs · South Downs · The Chilterns · Dartmoor

100km

Wars, sheep and deforestation

Most of Britain was once covered in **dense woodland**. Slowly this was cleared for farming. Charcoal burning further reduced woodland cover after the expansion of glass manufacture in the 14th Century. Deforestation accelerated in Tudor times with the demand for timber to build ships for a growing navy.

It was the **Napoleonic Wars** from 1799 which finally ended the ability of our upland areas to regenerate woodland. With the British army growing from 30,000 to 300,000 in a few decades, the demand for wool for the soldiers' uniforms saw a great

Elizabeth Thompson - Quatra Bras

expansion of **hill sheep farming**. In Scotland, thousands of poor farmers were thrown off the land to make way for sheep. This became known as the '**Highland Clearances**.' As sheep like grazing on young nutritious tree saplings, the **flocks prevented woodland regrowth**. Shallow soils became waterlogged, peaty and acidic, but plants such as heather thrived.

So the landscapes we think of as 'natural', from Snowdonia to the North York Moors, are not natural but a product of long-term **human activity** interacting with **physical processes.**

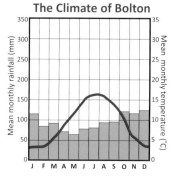

The Climate of Bolton

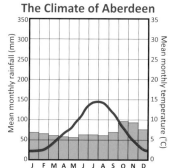

The Climate of Aberdeen

Sheep: hero or villain?
You decide....

"Grazing livestock is an intrinsic part of the upland landscape that is not only a major source of sheep and cattle but the backdrop to significant tourism, a home to a rich diversity of wildlife and an area that contains a wealth of history and culture."
National Farmers Union

"Sheep are the primary reason for the sad state of the British uplands. Partly as a result of their assaults, Wales now possesses less than one-third of the average forest cover of Europe."
George Monbiot, environmental journalist

KEY TERMS

Convectional rainfall: rain caused by the cooling of warm air as it rises above a heated land or sea surface.

Frontal rainfall: rain caused by the meeting of two different air masses, resulting in the warmer air rising and cooling: common in Britain as cold arctic air meets warm tropical air.

Relief rainfall: rain caused by the movement of moist air over mountains and hills resulting in the condensation of water into cloud droplets

fig.15 **Vixen Tor, Dartmoor**

Dartmoor's Granite Landscape.

Many upland landscapes are very closely associated with the underlying rock type. Granite is both resistant to erosion and impermeable. This leads to the formation of hills and mountains with **thin and waterlogged soils**. The underground **chemical weathering** of granite (see page 13) leads to the creation of dramatic **granite tors** on the surface.

The **impermeable granite** stops water percolating into the underlying rock. This results in waterlogged soils which become **peaty and acidic**. Rainwater flows off the waterlogged soils to create numerous surface streams. These flow rapidly downhill off the granite hilltops carving **deep v-shaped valleys.**

The **cold, waterlogged soils** do not lend themselves to arable farming. Dartmoor has developed a **pastoral landscape**, where hardy beef cattle, sheep and the famous Dartmoor ponies are reared.

The dramatic landscape has become an **important tourist attraction** with over 2.4 million visitors coming every year to the Dartmoor National Park. However, not all the park has permanent open access as the **Ministry of Defence** use almost 10% as a training ground and firing range. While this restricts access to some of the park during exercises, most is open to the public when training is not taking place. The Dartmoor Parks Authority is working to end live firing on Dartmoor.

fig.16 **Dartmoor Pony**

fig.17 **Yorkshire Dales**

Yorkshire's Limestone Dales

The Yorkshire Dales are dominated by a so-called **karst landscape,** resulting from the underlying carboniferous limestone. This has chemically weathered to form large tracts of **limestone pavement** (see p13). As the product of limestone weathering is soluble calcium bicarbonate, the **rendzina soil** here is very thin but fertile. It is ideal for growing grass. **Pastoral farming** dominates, with sheep on the higher ground and cattle on the lower slopes. The region is famous for its Wensleydale cheese.

The limestone is pervious - which means water can flow down through cracks. This helps to weather and erode underground caves and cavern systems. There are few surface streams, except where the water flows over **impermeable shales**. This can be seen at the famous resurgence at the base of Malham Cove.

There are many famous **potholes** through the Dales such as Gaping Gill. Here Fell Beck plunges 98 meters to the cavern floor. In the carbon dioxide-rich atmosphere of the caverns **calcite** is slowly precipitated out of solution to form sub-surface features of **stalactites, stalagmites** and **flowstone** curtains.

▲ fig.18 **Malham Cove with a rare waterfall, Dec. 2015**

At the end of the last glaciation (see p10), meltwater from the ice flowed over the surface carving out v-shaped river valleys. Today the water **flows underground** leaving 'dry valleys' and former waterfalls such as the 80 metre high **Malham Cove**.

Thinking it through

1. Describe and explain the **impact of hill sheep farming** on the upland landscapes of the British Isles. (8)

2. Outline the links between **soil types and agricultural land use** in the British isles. (4)

3. Using Fig.20, on page 10, describe the **distribution of glaciated uplands** in the UK. (4)

4. In relation to landscape erosion, outline why ice has a **greater potential erosive power** than liquid water. (4)

5. Using the OS map extract, on page 11, what feature of glacial erosion is found at grid reference 711 130 (1)

6. Name the **corrie tarns** shown on the map on page 11. (3)

What are the characteristics of our glaciated areas?

Ice, coupled with the rocks it carries frozen inside it, is one of the **most erosive agents** on Earth. This erosion takes place around ice sheets and valley glaciers. Today, ice cover is restricted to the high mountain ranges of the world, such as the **Andes, Alps** and **Himalayas**, or the high latitudes such as **Norway, Greenland, Alaska** and, of course, **Antarctica**. While there is ice at the North Pole, this is sea ice, floating over an ocean, and so cannot erode the land. Many of Britain's most dramatic landscapes were formed by ice over successive colder periods called 'glacials' or 'glaciations.'

During glacials, **valley glaciers** form high on **east and north** facing mountain slopes. Snow builds up year after year. This snow is compressed into ice crystals called **nevé** and then, as the air is excluded under pressure, into **glacial ice**. These source areas of glaciers are called **corries**.

As the ice builds up in the corrie its weight makes it move downhill. Meltwater freezes the ice to the rock face and then, as the ice moves, it **plucks** chunks of rock from the back wall of the corrie. These rocks are then scraped along the base of the corrie which is deepened by abra sion. As the ice moves in a rotation around the centre of the corrie, it begins to lift at its outer edge. This reduces erosion creating a **rock lip**. The ice then fractures into **deep crevasses** before flowing downhill along former river valleys.

Once the ice has melted, the **corrie** remains as a bowl-shaped hollow in the mountainside. This is often filled up to the rock lip with a roughly circular lake called a **corrie tarn**.

If two corries erode back to back, the hillside between them is eroded to leave a sharp, knifed-edged ridge called an **arête**. Should three or more corries erode the same mountain, the **arêtes** will join together near the summit to create a **pyramidal peak**. The broken rock fragments carried by the glacier are finally deposited when it melts to leave **moraine**.

fig.20 **Features of a valley glacier**

Nunatuk
Corrie
Corrie
Corrie
Crevasses
Truncated spurs
Snout
Terminal moraine
Meltwater

Britain's glaciated highlands

Skye
Rum
Arran
Western Highlands
Cairngorms
Loch Lomond and the Trossachs
Lake District
Snowdonia

abrasion **abra** *in a* in a

fig.19 **Britain's glaciated highlands**

KEY TERMS

Arête: a sharp knife-edged ridge separating two corries.

Corrie: an armchair shaped hollow high in the mountains where a glacier forms.

Glacial: colder period where ice sheets and valley glaciers advance.

Glacial trough: deep 'U-shaped' valley with steep sides and flat floor carved out of a river valley by a valley glacier.

Glacier: river of ice flowing slowly down from highland areas. European glaciers are found today in the Alps and Norway.

Interglacial: warmer period when glaciers and ice sheets retreat or melt altogether.

Ice Age: often confusing term which is used to refer to both the Pleistocene epoch and the colder glacials within it.

Pyramidal Peak: a mountain where three or more aretes join at the summit.

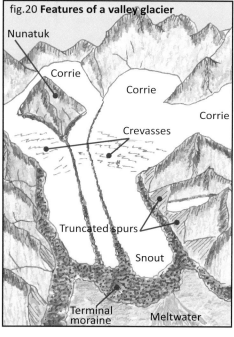

Fig.21 **Ice cover during the last glaciation**

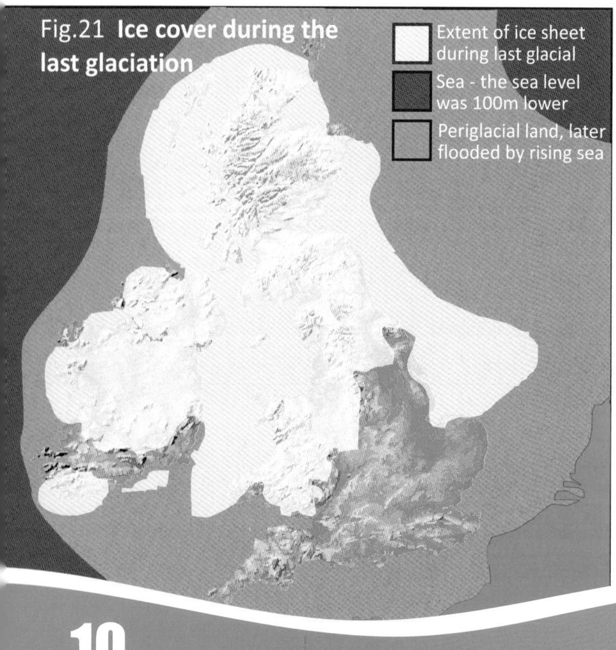

- Extent of ice sheet during last glacial
- Sea - the sea level was 100m lower
- Periglacial land, later flooded by rising sea

The Ice Age, glacials and inter-glacials

Around 2.5 million years ago, global temperatures began to fall as ocean and atmospheric circulation patterns changed. We had entered the **Pleistocene era** –the Ice Age. During this period global temperatures fell by as much a 9°C below today's average. Ice sheets spread outwards from the poles and mountain regions. As the ice spread it eroded the top surface layers of vegetation, soil and then the underlying rock.

There have been several colder periods called **glacials** during the Pleistocene, inter-spaced by warmer **inter-glacials**. We are currently about 11,500 years into the most recent inter-glacial, called **The Holocene.**

fig.22: **Glen Coe, Scottish glacial trough**

▼ fig.23: **Ordnance Survey map of Cadair Idris: 1:50,000**

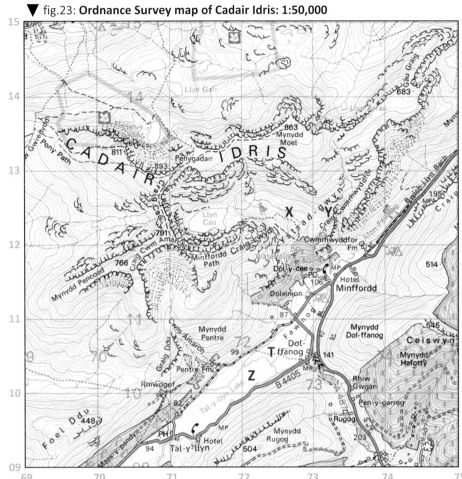

As glaciers join together, like the tributaries of a river, smaller glaciers dump their ice on top of the larger one, increasing the erosive power at the base of that glacier. A 500m thick glacier can exert a force of around 500 tonnes per square metre. The floor of the valley is deepened by **abrasion** while the interlocking spurs of the former river valley are ground away to create a deep steeped sided U-shaped valley called a **glacial trough** (marked with **T** on the map).

When the ice melts, the valleys of the tributary glaciers are left high above the floor of the glacial trough as **hanging valleys (X)**. The eroded interlocking spurs will appear as steep-faced **truncated spurs (Y)**. **Ribbon lakes (Z)** may fill floor of the valley.

fig.24: **Features of Glaciated Uplands**

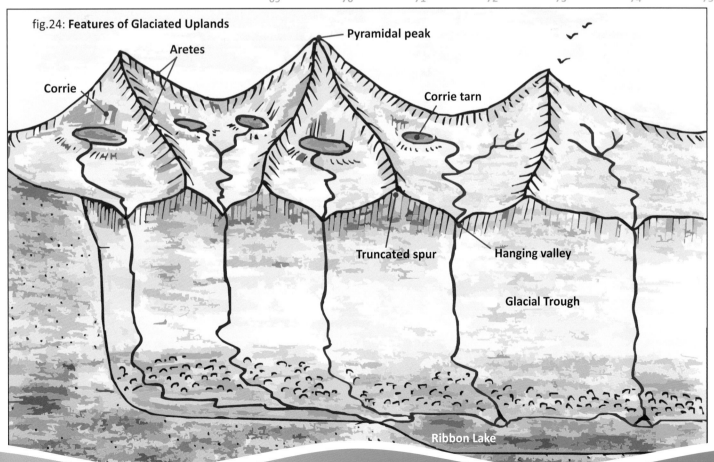

What is the role of weathering in landscape formation?

Weathering is the breakdown of rocks *in situ* (in one place) usually under the influence of a climatic element or biological factor. It **should not be confused with erosion** which is part of a three-fold process of erosion (the wearing away of rocks), transportation (removal to another location) and deposition (left in a new location.)

Mechanical weathering.

Mechanical weathering involves the **breakdown of a rock** into smaller pieces of that same rock, with **no change in the chemical composition** of the minerals in the rock.

There are a number of different types of mechanical weathering but the most common in the British Isles is **freeze-thaw weathering** (sometimes called **frost shattering**). In this process, water seeps into cracks in the rock. When temperatures fall below freezing the water turns to ice and expands. This expansion is the result of water forming a crystal lattice as it changes into ice. **The expanding ice can add stresses to the rock, widening the crack.**

When the ice melts the water can now seep further into the rock, only to expand again when it freezes. Over time the **repeated freezing and thawing of the rock widens the crack until the rock shatters** along the developing line of weaknesses.

This process is most effective when temperatures fluctuate around 0°C. This is the case at the tops of mountains in winter. It was also true for the whole of the British Isles immediately after the last glaciation, when temperatures were slowly warming. Freeze-thaw weathering results in **sharp, angular fragments of rock** which may build up to form **scree slopes**.

 1. Water seeps into a crack in the surface of a rock.

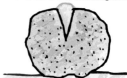 2. Temperatures fall below freezing and the water turns to ice, widening the crack.

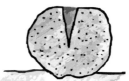 3. When the ice thaws and water seeps deeper into the now wider crack.

 4. Repeated freezing & melting of the water widens the crack, breaking up the rock.

▲ fig.25: **Freeze-thaw weathering in diagrams**

▼ fig.26: **A freeze-thaw weathered rock in the Lake District**

▲ fig.27: **Tree roots: a powerful weathering agent**

▼ fig.28: **Limpets can help weather a rocky shore**

Biological weathering

Living plants and animals can help to break down rocks. **Tree roots** can be very effective at breaking up underlying rock structures as they search for nutrients and water. **Lichens** secrete acids which chemically weather the rocks beneath them. Burrowing **worms** can help break down softer rocks. Even **rabbits** can help weather soft rocks while digging their burrows.

On rocky shores, **limpets** can help wear down the rock as they graze on algae and create hollows called **'homescars'** where they return at low tide (shown in bottom right-hand corner of figure 28). Some estimates have suggested limpets are responsible for the removal of up to **0.5mm of rock surface per year** on chalk shores. This doesn't sound like much but can add 50cm to erosion over 1000 years.

KEY TERMS

Biological weathering: the breakdown of rocks under the influence of plants or animals.

Chemical weathering: the breakdown of rocks as a result of chemical reactions which change one or more minerals within the rock.

Mechanical weathering: the breakdown of rocks into smaller fragment without any change in the mineral composition.

Weathering: the breakdown of rocks *in situ*, under the influence of a climatic or biotic agent.

12

There are a number of geomorphic processes which create distinctive landscapes.

How do chemical and biological agents weather rock?

Chemical weathering involves the breakdown of rock *in situ* as a result of a **change in the chemical composition** of the rock's minerals.

Chemical weathering of granite.

Granite is a physically tough rock made up of three minerals: **quartz, mica and feldspar**. It is extremely resistant to erosion. However, the mica will react with acids in rain water, supplemented by acids from plants and plant decay in the soils, to form **kaolin or china clay**. Once exposed at the surface the china clay can be washed away.

Once granite has begun to be chemically weathered, water may seep into the china clay thereby exposing the crytals to freeze-thaw weathering at the ground surface.

The combination of underground chemical weathering and freeze-thaw have helped produce the **granite tors** typical of the **Dartmoor National Park** (see p9) and other granite areas.

Chemical weathering of limestone.

Cretaceous chalk and **carboniferous limestone** are formed from the fossilised remains of microscopic sea shells made from **calcium carbonate**. In areas with these 'calcareous' rocks chemical weathering takes the form of **carbonation solution**.

The calcium carbonate of the limestone is attacked by **carbonic acid** in rainwater, reacting to form c**alcium bicarbonate**. Unlike calcium carbonate, the calcium bicarbonate is **soluble** and so dissolves in the rain water and is washed away. Unlike porous chalk, carboniferous limestone is impermeable to water and so carbonation can only take place at cracks in the rock. Carbonation solution helps to widen these cracks and is responsible for the formation of the dramatic areas of **limestone pavement** typical of the **Yorkshire Dales National Park** (see p9).

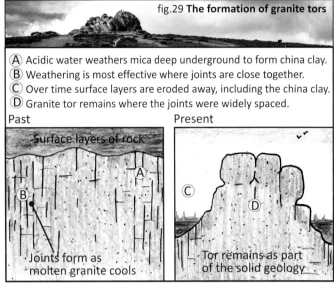

fig.29 **The formation of granite tors**

Ⓐ Acidic water weathers mica deep underground to form china clay.
Ⓑ Weathering is most effective where joints are close together.
Ⓒ Over time surface layers are eroded away, including the china clay.
Ⓓ Granite tor remains where the joints were widely spaced.

Past   Present

Surface layers of rock

Joints form as molten granite cools

Tor remains as part of the solid geology

▼ Fig.30 **The features of limestone pavement**

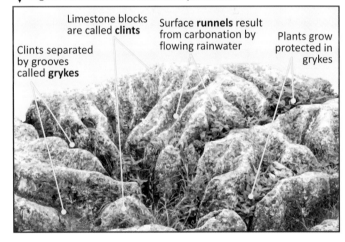

Limestone blocks are called **clints**

Surface **runnels** result from carbonation by flowing rainwater

Plants grow protected in grykes

Clints separated by grooves called **grykes**

Thinking it through

1. Evaluate the role of **weathering** in the formation of upland features of the British Isles. (8)

2. Explain why **granite**, which is resistant to physical erosion, may be more susceptible to chemical weathering. (6)

3. Describe and explain the formation of **limestone pavement** shown in figures 30 and 31. (6)

4. Describe the formation of a **scree slope** such as the one shown in figure 32. (4)

5. Suggest reasons why **freeze-thaw weathering** was more significant at the end of the last glacial period, but **chemical and biological weathering** were less significant than they are today. (6)

6. Draw a single diagram of **Haytor** (figure 33) to indicate the general features of a granite tor. **Add annotations** to explain the features shown. (4)

Fig.31 **Limestone pavement, Malham Cove**

Fig.33 **Haytor, Dartmoor National Park**

Fig.32 **Scree slope, Gordale Scar**

There are a number of geomorphic processes which create distinctive landscapes.

What is the cause and effect of mass movement?

The term **mass movement** refers to the downwards movement of weathered material, called **regolith**, under the **influence of gravity**. It is different from erosion and transportation under the influence of an agent such as water or ice. However, there is often water involved as its presence can weaken the structure of a slope making **sliding** or **slumping** more likely.

Soil creep is one of the slowest types of mass movement. **Landslides** and **slumps** are very rapid movements, where a whole section of a slope moves rapidly downhill.

Landslides tend to occur where the weaknesses in the rock strata, such as joints or bedding planes, **lie parallel to the angle of the slope**. During landslides blocks of rock detach from the slope and move down a **flat rupture surface**. The blocks of rock will often shatter on reaching the base of the slope. Rock slides can be caused by **heavy rain** lubricating the weakness in the rock strata or by **earthquakes** which can break the rock strata apart.

Rotational slumping is common where softer rocks, such as sands, overlie more resistant or impermeable rocks such as clay. On the **Holderness** and **North Norfolk** coasts glacial till allows rain water to pass through the rock until it reaches impermeable clay below. The rainwater flowing over the clay **weakens the boundary zone** where the different rock types meet.

As slumping occurs, a section of cliff moves down along a **curved rupture surface**, leaving dipping **terraces** on the cliff face and piles of slumped material at the cliff base. This slumped material is washed away by wave action on the coast, exposing and weakening the base of the cliff. This allows further slumping to occur resulting in significant coastal erosion.

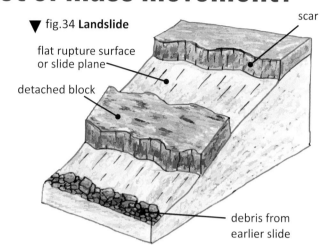

▼ fig.34 **Landslide**

scar
flat rupture surface or slide plane
detached block
debris from earlier slide

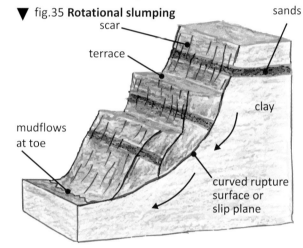

▼ fig.35 **Rotational slumping**

sands
scar
terrace
mudflows at toe
clay
curved rupture surface or slip plane

fig.36 **Slumping, Alum Bay, Isle of Wight**

fig.37 **Cliff collapse, Norfolk coast**

Soil creep

Soil creep is the slow movement of soil down a slope at rates below **1 cm per year**. It is an almost continuous process caused by the expansion and contraction of the soil. This happens for two reasons.

During cold spells the surface layer of the soil freezes. As the water turns to ice it expands lifting the soil outwards, away from the underlying layers. This is called **heave**. As the ice melts, the particles of soil fall back under gravity, now slightly lower than their original position.

During wet and dry periods soils can contract during droughts, especially on soils with a **high clay composition**. When the rains return the soil **expands, then contracts again** during the next dry spell. This can result in slow movement downhill.

Soil creep can result in the damage to farm fences and walls, as well as the creation of miniature ridges or **terracettes** along the slope.

KEY TERMS

Land slide: the movement of land downhill on an unstable slope.

Mass movement: the downhill movement of weathered material or soil under the force of gravity.

Slumping: a rapid mass movement in which an large section of slope or cliff moves down slope along a water-saturated 'shear plane.'

Soil creep: the very slow movement of soil down a slope due to gravity. This can lead to the formation of small ridges called terracettes.

14

There are a number of geomorphic processes which create distinctive landscapes.

Rivers: what are erosion and transportation processes?

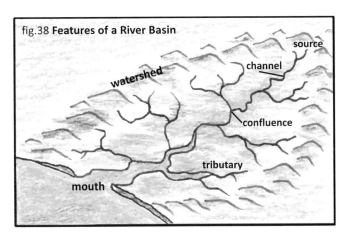

fig.38 **Features of a River Basin**

watershed

source

channel

confluence

tributary

mouth

A **drainage basin** is the area of land drained by a river and its tributaries. The basin, or **catchment**, is boarded by the **watershed**, the area of higher ground which separates one river basin from its neighbouring basins.

Drainage basins represent the land section of the hydrological cycle. They collect water that has fallen as **precipitation** (rain, snow, sleet or hail) and transport that water which doesn't evaporate, or get taken up by plants, back to the sea.

All rivers have a **source**, the area where rainwater begins to flow downhill in a noticeable groove or **channel**. Smaller streams or rivers joining the main channel are called **tributaries**, which join at **confluences**. The source is the furthest point from the **mouth,** where the river water is discharged into the sea or a lake.

Did you know?

Britain's largest river basin is the **Severn** with an area of 11,420km^2. In contrast, the catchment of the **River Valency**, which flooded Boscastle in 2004, is just 40km^2. Even Britain's largest rivers are small by global standards. The combined basins of the **Ganges–Brahmaputra** which flow into the sea through Bangladesh cover 1,600,000km^2. The **Amazon** dwarfs all rivals with an area of 6,150,000km^2 - 30% of the total area of South America.

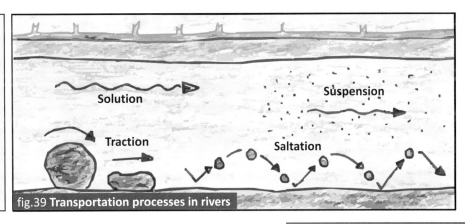

Solution

Suspension

Traction

Saltation

fig.39 **Transportation processes in rivers**

Transportation in rivers

Rivers not only transport water they also carry **sediment**: rock particles that have been eroded along the river's course and are that are transported downstream. This sediment is referred to as the river's **load**. **Transportation** of the river's load occurs through four distinct processes.

Traction is the **rolling or dragging** of large rocks – the bed load - along the river bed.

Saltation is the **bouncing** or leap-frogging of smaller bedload such as sand grains along the river bed.

Suspension is when fine silts and clay particles are **carried within the water column** itself. Suspended load makes the river water appear turbid or murky.

Solution is the transportation of dissolved salts and minerals in **ionic form**, such as calcium and bicarbonate ions. These dissolved minerals add to the salts in the oceans.

Things to remember

Abrasion and hydraulic action are the key processes of river erosion. Moving water and sediment wear away the river's banks and bed. This creates **erosional features** such as **v-shaped valleys**, **interlocking spurs** and **waterfalls**.

River erosion

Rivers erode their channels using both the moving water and the grinding effect of the moving sediment. There are four processes of erosion which occur in rivers.

Abrasion or corrasion is the grinding of rocks against other rocks wearing them away. Large, angular bedload is moved by traction. This tends to result in **vertical erosion** and deepens the river

channel. Fine, suspended load acts as a 'liquid sandpaper' and results in **lateral (sideways) erosion** at the river banks.

Hydraulic action is the force and weight of the moving water causing erosion. Water can compress air into existing cracks. This can then expand explosively, weakening the banks.

Attrition is the breakdown of sediment into smaller

fig.40 **Glen Rosa Waters, Isle of Arran**

fragments, as the result of collisions with other moving sediment.

Solution or **corrosion** is the break-up of rocks into **soluble ions** as the product of

chemical reactions. For example, the calcium carbonate in limestone reacts with mildly acidic river water to create soluble calcium bicarbonate.

15

There are a number of geomorphic processes which create distinctive landscapes.

How does a river long profile change?

The **long profile** of a river describes the changes in **height and gradient** as it moves from its source to its mouth at base level. In most rivers the base level is the sea. The long profile can be divided into three sections – the **upper course**, **middle course** and **lower course**.

▼ fig.41 **The long profile and valley cross-profiles of a river basin.**

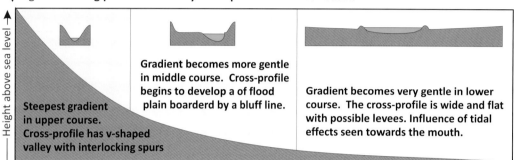

Height above sea level →

Steepest gradient in upper course. Cross-profile has v-shaped valley with interlocking spurs

Gradient becomes more gentle in middle course. Cross-profile begins to develop a of flood plain boarderd by a bluff line.

Gradient becomes very gentle in lower course. The cross-profile is wide and flat with possible levees. Influence of tidal effects seen towards the mouth.

← Distance from source →

In the **upper course** the channel is full of angular boulders which create a lot of friction. Most of the river's energy is used overcoming this friction. Very little energy is left for erosion and transportation. However, **after heavy rain or snow melt,** as the river levels rise, friction is reduced and the velocity increases. Now the river can move larger rocks and boulders. This large sediment is moved by **traction** and is dragged along the channel bed **eroding it vertically**. This creates deep v-shaped valleys.

In the **middle course**, as more water joins the channel, more fine sediment is carried in suspension. This erodes the banks laterally (side to side). **Smaller bed load**, reduced in size and angularity by attrition, is less able to erode vertically. As a result, **the long profile becomes less steep.** The loss of energy results in **deposition.** This occurs alongside the erosion and helps to form meanders.

In the **lower course** the river is carrying much more water. Despite a reduction in gradient, it tends to flow faster within its wider and more efficient channel. However, when it reaches the sea, or bursts its banks during a flood, the **loss of energy results in deposition** of sediment. This helps in the formation of features such as deltas and levees.

V-shaped valleys and interlocking spurs

In the **upper course** of the river the channel is **narrow and shallow and often choked with large, angular boulders** creating friction. At times of high discharge the river becomes deeper and so it can flow faster. The faster and more turbulent flow is able to move more sediment and larger sizes of bedload. It does this by traction. The **heavy bedload scrapes along the channel bed** deepening it by **abrasion**. As the water levels recede, the newly deepened banks are now exposed to weathering, such as **freeze-thaw** - and over time parts of the bank collapse into the channel. This adds more rocks to the bedload.

fig.42 **V-shaped valley and interlocking spurs**

This process is repeated with the valley getting deeper over time and developing a **distinctive V-shaped cross-profile**.

As the river water flows down the V-shaped valley it is forced to move around areas of more resistant rock. It begins to zig-zag from side to side leaving **interlocking spurs**, or ridges of rock, extending out into the valley.

These **interlocking spurs** are found on the concave bends on alternate sides of the river. They appear to overlap or interlock like the teeth of a zip. It is these interlocking spurs which **restrict the view up the river valley**.

KEY TERMS

Abrasion: The wearing away of rocks by the action of moving rocks and sand grinding against them. This is sometimes called corrasion.

Attrition: the break down of rocks by their collision with other moving rocks.

Deposition: the laying down of sediment as the result in a fall in river velocity.

Erosion: the wearing away of rock and its removal to another place.

Hydraulic action: erosion by the weight and velocity of the moving water. The moving water may compress air in cracks which can then expand explosively.

Saltation: the movement of sand grains in a leap-frogging, bouncing motion along the river bed.

Solution: the removal of rock minerals in dissolved, ionic form. This is sometimes called corrosion.

Solution: the transportation of dissolved salts in ionic form.

Suspension: the movement of fine silts and clays held in the water column.

Traction: the movement of larger rocks in the bedload by rolling or dragging along the river bed.

Transportation: the method by which eroded material (sediment) is moved to another place.

There are a number of geomorphic processes which create distinctive landscapes.

How do waterfalls and gorges form?

Waterfalls occur where a river experiences an **increase in gradient close to 90°**. Cap rock waterfalls, such as **Thornton Force in Yorkshire,** are the result of a river flowing from a resistant rock onto a less-resistant rock downstream.

The less-resistant rock is **eroded faster** creating a step in the river. This results in an increase in river velocity at the waterfall. This further increases the erosion of the channel bed by **hydraulic action.** Over time, a **plunge pool** forms at the base of the fall. **Undercutting** of the softer rock behind the waterfall leads to the formation of an overhang. Over time the unsupported cap rock collapses into the river and the waterfall **retreats upstream.**

The collapsed cap rock adds to the abrasive capacity of bedload in the plunge pool grinding downwards as it is moved by the swirling water.

Repeated collapses result in the formation of a steep-sided **gorge of recession** forming downstream of the waterfall.

fig.43 **Thornton Force, River Twiss**

KEY TERMS

Delta: a depositional feature formed when a river deposits sediment at its mouth to create new, low-lying land in the sea or lake.

Interlocking spur: feature of the upper course restricting the view upstream, formed where the river zig-zags between ridges of rock on alternate sides of the river.

Levee: parallel ridges of deposited sediment running along the banks of a river, often leaving the river flowing above its flood plain.

Meanders: bends in a river's course formed by erosion and deposition. Meanders increase the sinuosity or 'bendiness' of a river.

Oxbow lake: a crescent shaped lake formed from a sealed-off meander bend.

Rapids: a steep section of a rivers course indicated by rapidly flowing, white water and often found where there are alternating bands of harder and softer rocks.

V-shaped valley: cross-profile of a river in the upper course created by intense vertical erosion and mass movement from the valley sides.

Waterfall: a 90°, vertical drop in a river's long profile.

Thinking it through

▼ fig.45 **The formation of a waterfall**

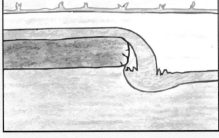

1. Make larger copies of the two diagrams above and add three annotations to each to explain the erosional processes and sequences involved in the formation of a cap-rock **waterfall**. (6)

2. Describe the processes in the formation of a river **gorge**. (4)

3. Outline the processes of **erosion** that may occur within a river. (4)

4. Describe the way that a river can **transport** its load. (4)

Waterfalls do not only form where resistant rock overlies less resistant rock. They can also form when rivers flow out of **hanging valleys** into the glacial trough below. They can be found where a river flows over the edge of a **plateau** such as with Angel Falls in Venezuela which is the world's tallest at 978m.

fig.44 **Angel Falls**

Another cause is where a river has gained more energy from a relative fall in sea level. This is a process called **rejuvenation** and is common in creating **'knickpoint' waterfalls** in the middle and lower course of rivers. These are common on the west coast of Scotland where the land has been rising slowly since the weight of glacial ice was removed after the last glaciation.

fig.46 **The Garbh Allt, Glen Rosa, Arran**

Rivers create a range of landforms which change with distance from their source within a river basin.

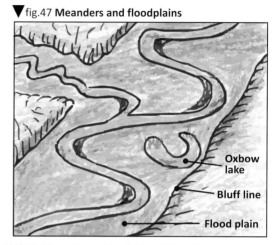

What are meanders, oxbow lakes and floodplains?

As the size of the river's **bed load** is reduced by **attrition** and the amount of suspended load increases, the river experiences a reduction in vertical erosion of the channel bed. There is an **increase in the lateral erosion** of the banks.

As the river attempts to move water past shallow areas of the channel called **riffles** it erodes one bank creating a deeper channel and steep **river cliff**. On the opposite side of the channel, where river flow is slower, deposition begins to occur creating a shallow zone with gentle **slip-off slope**. This erosion and deposition create a bending channel which is referred to as a **meander**.

The **asymmetrical shape of the channel** begins to create a **corkscrewing** motion in the water movement. This is called **helicoidal flow**. Helicoidal flow transports sediment eroded from the river cliff of one bend and deposits it on the opposite side of the channel on the slip-off slope downstream. At times of lower discharge the top of the slip-off slope is exposed as a **river beach**.

▼ fig.47 **Meanders and floodplains**

Oxbow lake
Bluff line
Flood plain

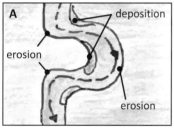

fig.48 **Cross-section of a meander**

The formation of oxbow lakes

▼ fig.49 **Oxbow lakes**

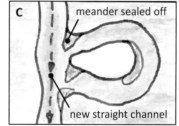

A) As meanders develop, **erosion on the outside of the bend** and **deposition on the inside** make the meander more **sinuous**. The fastest flow corkscrews from side to side

C) In time the neck is cut through to create a **new straight channel**. Fastest flow is now in the centre of the channel and **deposition begins to close up the former meander**

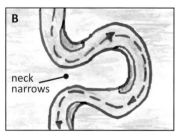

B) Over time the **neck of the meander narrows** as the outsides of two bends come closer together. This forms what is known as a **swan-neck meander.**

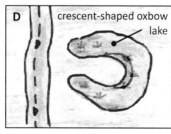

D) Once fully sealed off, a **crescent-shaped oxbow lake** is created within the flood plain. This slowly fills with alluvium and decaying vegetation to leave an **oxbow scar**.

Flood plains: a feature of erosion and deposition

Erosion, by **hydraulic action and abrasion**, on the outside of bends results in meanders **migrating downstream**. This movement results in the river eroding a flat area on either side of its channel. This is called a **flood plain**. This flat area receives excess waters when the river bursts its banks. The flood plain is bordered by a ridge of land called the **bluff line**. This ridge marks the outer edge of the meanders migration.

The river's **discharge will increase**, as it receives more water from tributaries, surface run-off and groundwater flow. Channel width increases along with discharge. This allows for a greater radius of the river's meanders and results in a **widening flood plain** as the river itself widens downstream.

During floods, standing water over the flood plain will **deposit fine silts and clay particles**. This is the river's suspended load. This **alluvium** builds up the level of the flood plain and helps to create rich and fertile soils.

▼ fig.50 **Meandering channel in a Scottish river**

18

Rivers create a range of landforms which change with distance from their source within a river basin.

How do levees form in the lower course of a river?

In the **lower course** of a river the channel is **wide and deep**. There is little friction. The river is able to **transport water at faster velocities** than in the upper course where friction from a narrow channel is greater.

fig.51 **Levee on the River Irvine, Scotland**

Levee has been stabilised by trees

However, when a river bursts its banks during a flood there is a sudden increase in friction, as the water flows out onto the flood plain. Velocity is reduced and the river **deposits the material** it is carrying. The coarsest sediments are deposited first. This creates a **small natural embankment** along the river bank. This coarse material is cemented together by the finer silts and clays carried by the river. The **finest alluvium is deposited on the flood plain** away from the channel. **Repeated flooding increases the height of these embankments**, which are called **levees**.

At times of lower discharge and so lower velocities, **sediment is deposited on the channel bed**. This **raises the bed**, keeping match with the rising height of the levees. In time both the levees and channel bed rise until the river is **flowing above the level of its flood plain**.

If levees collapse the resulting floods can be very severe. In many places the natural levees are strengthened and maintained to ensure they do not burst. In some places levees are **artificially heightened** to stop the river flooding onto its lower flood plain.

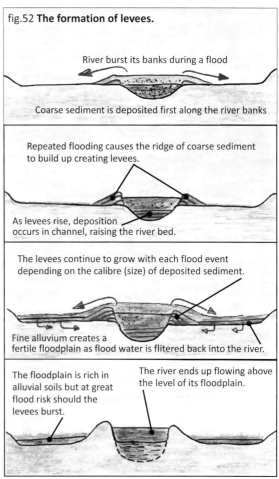

fig.52 **The formation of levees.**

River burst its banks during a flood

Coarse sediment is deposited first along the river banks

Repeated flooding causes the ridge of coarse sediment to build up creating levees.

As levees rise, deposition occurs in channel, raising the river bed.

The levees continue to grow with each flood event depending on the calibre (size) of deposited sediment.

Fine alluvium creates a fertile floodplain as flood water is flitered back into the river.

The floodplain is rich in alluvial soils but at great flood risk should the levees burst.

The river ends up flowing above the level of its floodplain.

Thinking it through

1. What is an **interlocking spur**? (2)

2. Describe and explain the formation of **V-shaped** valleys (4)

3. Define what is meant by a **floodplain.** (2)

4. What is meant by the term **long profile** of a river? (2)

5. What is a **valley cross-profile**? (2)

6. Describe and explain the formation of **river levees**. (4)

7. Explain why river **sediment** (the load), tends to become smaller and more rounded downstream. (4)

8. Describe the features of a river **meander**. (4)

9. With the aid of a diagram(s) describe the formation of an **oxbow lake**. (6)

10. **Floodplains**, in the middle course of a river, are the product of both erosion and deposition. Discuss the role of both these processes in the creation of **floodplains**. (6)

11. Describe and explain the changes in a river's **long profile** and valley **cross profiles** along a river's course. (8)

12. Rivers tend to flow faster in their lower course despite a reduction in the channel's gradient. Explain the reasons for this change in **velocity**. (4)

Your Revision checklist

You must make sure you are confident about the **distribution** of areas of **upland, lowland** and **glaciated** landscapes. This should include an overview of the **distinctive characteristics** of these landscapes including their **geology, climate** and **human activity** (pages 4-11).

You must be able to define the main **geomorphic processes** including types of **weathering** (mechanical, chemical and biological), **mass movement** (sliding and slumping), **erosion** (abrasion, hydraulic action, attrition and solution), **transportation** (traction, saltation, suspension and solution) and **deposition** (pages 12-15).

You should be clear about the formation of the range of **landforms created by rivers** and how they change with **distance from their source** within a river basin. The key landforms are **waterfalls, gorges, V-shaped valleys, floodplains, levees, meanders** and **oxbow lakes** (pages 16-19).

Rivers create a range of landforms which change with distance from their source within a river basin.

How do waves and other processes shape the coast?

The coast is the narrow zone between land and sea. It is constantly changing. It is affected by a wide variety of influences and processes.

Waves are created by the wind blowing over the sea's surface. Large waves contain lots of energy, while small waves have less energy. The strength or energy of a wave is determined by 3 factors: the length of **time** the wind blew, the **speed** of the wind and the **distance** of sea over which the wind blew. This last factor is called the **fetch**.

On the south west coast of England and Ireland, the fetch is very long, extending across the Atlantic Ocean. This is the direction of **Britain's prevailing wind.** Waves formed by distant storms with a long fetch are called **high energy waves**. Waves formed by more local winds are referred to as **low energy waves**. Waves have different characteristics which create different shapes or '**profile**s' of the beaches they break against.

The type of waves approaching the coastlines of Britain change throughout

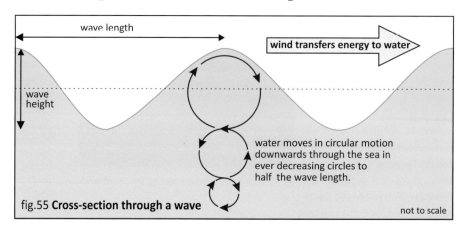

fig.55 **Cross-section through a wave**

wave length

wind transfers energy to water

wave height

water moves in circular motion downwards through the sea in ever decreasing circles to half the wave length.

not to scale

the year, with changes in global wind and weather patterns. As a result the profile of beaches may also change throughout the year.

Some waves, often formed by distant storms are described as **constructive**. These waves tend to break up the beach, pushing beach material upwards with a strong **swash**. Other waves, formed by local storms, are described as **destructive**. These break downwards and drag sediment down the beach in the strong **backwash.**

fig.54 **Waves transport immense energy.**

Coastal erosion

Wave erosion can been seen in action on a rocky coastline. Erosion is greatest where the waves crash against the **base of a cliff**. Wave action is concentrated in the inter-tidal zone – between high tide and low tide.

Wave pounding, and **abrasion** will create a small **wave-cut notch** at the base of the cliff. This could get larger and deeper over time, creating a sea cave, until the rock above is left unsupported and it collapses. Over more time, the collapsed cliff material is further broken down by the waves and **transported away**. The process of creating a new wave cut notch begins again.

Repeated collapses results in the cliff line **retreating inland** while a

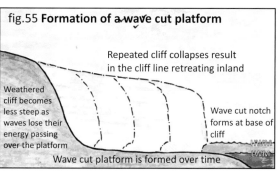

fig.55 **Formation of a wave cut platform**

Repeated cliff collapses result in the cliff line retreating inland

Weathered cliff becomes less steep as waves lose their energy passing over the platform

Wave cut notch forms at base of cliff

HWM
LWM

Wave cut platform is formed over time

gently sloping expanse of land extends from the cliff base towards the sea. This is called a **wave-cut platform** and is exposed at low tide. As erosion of the cliffs continues, the wave cut platform become so wide that it absorbs all the energy from the incoming waves as they pass through the shallow water. This reduces erosion at the cliff base.

Now '**sub-aerial**' (land) processes, such as **mass movement** and **weathering**, can begin to breakdown the cliff face. As a result, the cliff becomes less steep as the years go by.

There are a range of landforms within the coastal landscape.

What are the erosional features of a rocky headland?

Cliffs tend to form where the rocks are **resistant to erosion**. Where there are alternating bands of different rocks, headlands and bays may form. Headlands are found where the rock is more resistant to erosion. Bays are found where the rock is less resistant.

There are always weaknesses in the rocks, called cracks and joints. Erosion becomes concentrated at these weaknesses. **Hydraulic power and abrasion combine** to widen and deepen the weakness. Initially, cracks are expanded to form **sea caves**.

When the wave energy is concentrated by wave refraction on both sides of a headland, cracks may be eroded from both sides. The two caves may eventually join to form an **arch**.

As wave erosion continues to widen the arch, the roof will become unsupported. It will collapse onto the wave cut platform. The former outer edge of the cliff is now left isolated as a column of rock called a **stack**.

In time erosion will wear away the base of the sea stack so that it too collapses. This leaves the stack's base as a **stump**.

▼ fig.56 **Am Buachaille, Sutherland**

KEY TERMS

Abrasion: pebbles, sand and shingle thrown at a cliff by the waves act to wear it way.

Attrition: collisions between rocks rolled up and down in the breaking waves making them smaller and more rounded.

Hydraulic pressure: waves compress air in cracks, increasing pressure and then releasing it explosively when the wave recedes. This weakens the rock face.

Sea arch: A wave eroded passage through a headland, created by the connection of caves forming on both sides of the headland.

Sea cave: A large hole in the base of the cliff caused by waves eroding cracks in the cliff face.

Sea stack: An isolated pillar of rock formed by the collapse of the roof of a sea arch.

Sea stump: The remains of a sea stack that has collapsed as a result of erosion at its base.

Subaerial processes: erosion and weathering processes associated with the landscapes.

Wave cut notch: A feature of erosion at the base of a cliff created where wave energy is concentrated between the high and low water marks.

Wave-cut platform: A rocky, gently-shelving ledge at sea level marking the base of a retreating cliff.

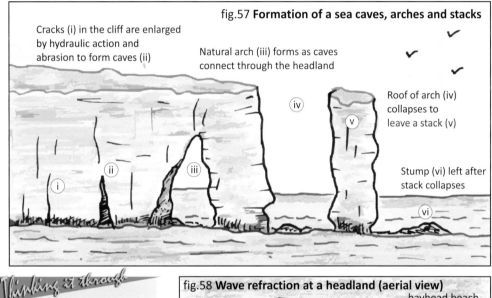

fig.57 **Formation of a sea caves, arches and stacks**

Cracks (i) in the cliff are enlarged by hydraulic action and abrasion to form caves (ii)

Natural arch (iii) forms as caves connect through the headland

Roof of arch (iv) collapses to leave a stack (v)

Stump (vi) left after stack collapses

Thinking it through

1. Define what is meant by the term **fetch**. (1)

2. Explain how **Britain** is affected by winds with a variety of different **fetches**. (3)

3. With the **aid of a diagram**, describe the formation of a **wave-cut platform**. (4)

4. Describe and explain the formation of two or more **erosional features** of a rocky headland. (6)

5. Explain what is meant by a **sub-aerial process**. (2)

6. Describe the relationship between **wind and waves** at sea (3)

7. Contrast the **swash** and **backwash** of a wave. (3)

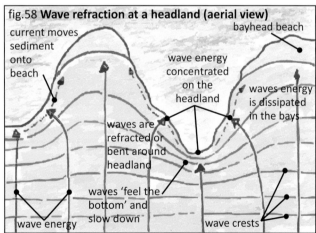

fig.58 **Wave refraction at a headland (aerial view)**

current moves sediment onto beach

bayhead beach

wave energy concentrated on the headland

waves energy is dissipated in the bays

waves are refracted or bent around headland

waves 'feel the bottom' and slow down

wave energy

wave crests

As a wave approaches the coast its base **experiences friction** with the rising sea bed and **begins to slow down**. When the shoreline is marked by bays and headlands, the wave 'feels the bottom' first at the headland. This acts to swing or **refract** the wave onto the headland. Its **energy is concentrated at the headland** while being dissipated within the bay. This wave refraction allows the headland to be eroded from both sides. The build up of water at the headland creates a **longshore current**. This moves eroded material from the headland to the bay to be deposited as a **bayhead beach**.

21

There are a range of landforms within the coastal landscape.

How do different waves help shape beaches?

Sediment size and beach profiles

fig.59 **Steep limestone gravel beach at Penrhyn Bay**

fig.60 **Gentle sandy beach at Talacre**

Where **eroded sediment is deposited** on the shore, beaches form. Many beaches form in sheltered areas such as bays. Others are the product of material being moved along the shoreline. **Beaches can change shape** or **profile** as a result of changing wave patterns and the supply of sediment.

On a sandy beach the swash carries material up the beach and then carries it down again in the backwash. This creates a gently shelving beach with a low angle.

However, **gravel and shingle beaches have a much steeper gradient than sandy beaches**. On a shingle beach the swash carries material up the beach but, because the backwash is able to quickly infiltrate into the gaps between the pebbles, its backwash has little energy. Sediment is not pulled down the beach and so the beach becomes steeper.

During storms, coarse material is thrown up above the high tide mark (called the wrack line) by the breaking waves. This creates a ridge called a **storm beach**.

Changing weather patterns throughout a year can result in beaches become wider and flatter during summer months but narrower and steeper during winter storms.

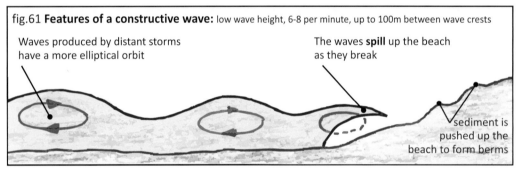

fig.61 **Features of a constructive wave:** low wave height, 6-8 per minute, up to 100m between wave crests

Waves produced by distant storms have a more elliptical orbit

The waves **spill** up the beach as they break

sediment is pushed up the beach to form berms

Constructive Waves

Constructive waves tend to be formed by far away weather events and have an **elliptical wave orbit**. As they break on the shoreline they **'spill'** up the beach. The **strong swash** created by the spilling wave carries material up the beach to create ridges, called **berms**. The **backwash is weaker** as it is disrupted by the next incoming swash. Beaches dominated by constructive waves tend to be **wide**. They provide excellent protection against coastal flooding and storm damage.

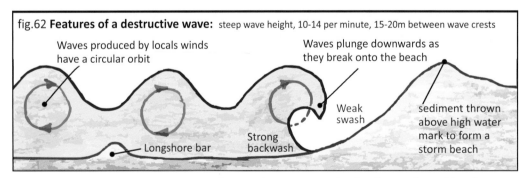

fig.62 **Features of a destructive wave:** steep wave height, 10-14 per minute, 15-20m between wave crests

Waves produced by locals winds have a circular orbit

Waves plunge downwards as they break onto the beach

Weak swash

Strong backwash

Longshore bar

sediment thrown above high water mark to form a storm beach

Destructive Waves

Destructive waves tend to be the product of local storms in nearby seas. The have a more **circular wave orbit** than constructive waves. As they break on the shoreline they **'plunge'** downwards onto the beach. This creates a **weak swash but a strong backwash**. The backwash can carry material away from the beach to be deposited as a **longshore bar**. The plunging wave may throw material into the air above the high water mark to form a **storm beach**.

KEY TERMS

Bay Bar: a depositional feature similar to a spit but which stretches across a coastal inlet or small river mouth.

Beach: zone of deposited material that extends from the low water line to the limit of storm waves.

Cuspate foreland: A feature of coastal deposition where land extends into the sea as a result of alternating directions of longshore drift.

Spit: A depositional feature where a finger of land extends into the sea where the coastline changes direction, such as at a river mouth.

Tombolo: a depositional feature similar to a spit which connects the mainland to an offshore island by way of a deposited finger of sediment.

How is beach material transported by longshore drift?

Longshore drift is the process by which beach sediment, such as cobbles, shingle, gravel and sand, is moved along a shoreline beach. This **movement happens in the wave or surf zone**. As the tide moves in and out, up and down the beach twice a day, the waves are able to move significant quantities of material along the shoreline each year.

Where a beach is protected on both sides by rocky

fig.64 **Sea Palling, Norfolk.** Offshore artificial reefs have been constructed to intercept wave energy and reduce the impact of longshore drift and coastal erosion

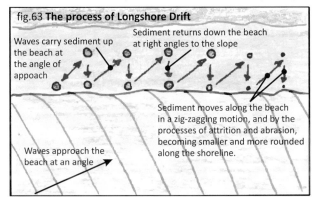

fig.63 **The process of Longshore Drift**

Waves carry sediment up the beach at the angle of appoach

Sediment returns down the beach at right angles to the slope

Sediment moves along the beach in a zig-zagging motion, and by the processes of attrition and abrasion, becoming smaller and more rounded along the shoreline.

Waves approach the beach at an angle

headlands, or the wind blows directly at right-angles to the shore, longshore drift will be minimal. These are called **swash-aligned** beaches.

Longshore drift happens on beaches and coastlines in which the **waves tend to break at an angle to the beach** itself. These are called **drift-aligned beaches.** On these coasts the prevailing winds do not blow directly at right angles. The waves also arrive at an angle.

On coasts with long stretches of beach, such as in North Wales or the Holderness Coast in Yorkshire, longshore drift can move eroded material great distances.

As a wave breaks onto a beach the swash will wash material **up the beach at the same angle as the approaching wave.** However, the **backwash returns down the beach under gravity,** so it flows down the slope at right angles. The backwash brings the transported sediment

down the beach **a little further on** from where it was moved by the breaking wave. Successive waves will move the sediment in a **zig-zagging motion along the beach.**

The longshore drift acts, with **abrasion and attrition**, to **round the sediment,** as it is rolled up and down the beach in the wave zone. It also acts to **sort the sediment by size**. The finest sands are transported further along the beach, while pebbles and gravel remains travel more slowly. The beach becomes sorted by size of sediment along the coast.

Where longshore drift is prevented from occurring, perhaps because of **sea defences up the coast,** beaches may suffer **erosion**. Those beaches receiving less sediment will become thinner as the existing beach is transported away by longshore drift.

Thinking it through

1. What is meant by the term **beach?** (2)

2. Explain how the **size of beach sediment** can affect the shape or **profile of a beach**. (4)

3. Contrast **drift-aligned** and **swash-aligned** beaches. (3)

4. With the **aid of a diagram**, explain **longshore drift** and describe how it can **sort sediment by size** along the coast. (6)

5. Explain why beaches on the English Channel, south-west coast of England may receive **more constructive waves** than the coastlines of the North Sea on the east coast. (6)

6. Explain the impact on the width of beaches of building sea defences further up the coast, which **prevent longshore drift**. (4)

7. With reference to an example, describe the formation of a **sea spit**. (4)

8. What is meant by the term **destructive wave?** (4)

▼ fig.65 **Features of deposition and longshore drift**

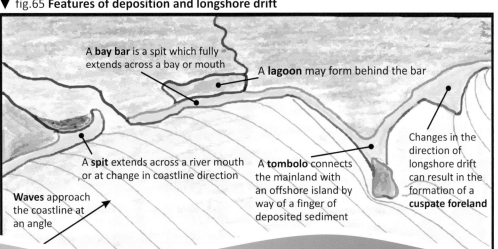

A **bay bar** is a spit which fully extends across a bay or mouth

A **lagoon** may form behind the bar

A **spit** extends across a river mouth or at change in coastline direction

A **tombolo** connects the mainland with an offshore island by way of a finger of deposited sediment

Changes in the direction of longshore drift can result in the formation of a **cuspate foreland**

Waves approach the coastline at an angle

23

There are a range of landforms within the coastal landscape.

Case Study: The Afon Ogwen, from source to mouth.

The **Afon Ogwen** is a roughly **20km long** river in the north of the **Snowdonia National Park** (*afon is the Welsh word for river*). The river's source is on the slopes of the **Carneddau** mountains, at 750 metres on the northern flanks of the **Ogwen Valley**.

In some ways the Afon Ogwen is **very typical** of most rivers: its **discharge increases as you move downstream**. The **width and depth of the channel also increase** as the river moves from source to mouth. The river generally **flows faster towards the mouth** (despite a decline in gradient). The high level of friction found in the upper course is gradually reduced as the river become wider and deeper.

What is **not typical** of this river is that the two valleys it flows though were not eroded by the Afon Ogwen itself. They were eroded by a glacier. These 'rivers of ice' filled the Ogwen and Nant Ffrancon valleys during the last glaciation (see fig.78). The Afon Ogwen can be described as a **misfit stream**: a river than is too small to have eroded the valley in which it flows.

The glacial history of the Afon Ogwen can be seen in the features through which it flows. Close to the source (at 650m above sea level) is a corrie tarn called **Ffynnon Lloer**. As the river leaves the tarn it tumbles around 350 metres in just 1.5

fig.66 **Ogwen Falls, looking down into the Nant Ffrancon**

kilometres, down the sides of the **Ogwen valley** which is a glacial trough. It then flows into a ribbon lake called **Llyn Ogwen**. The lake bed was eroded deeply by glacial ice but then subsequently filled with water after the ice melted.

From Llyn Ogwen the river plunges 100m down the **Ogwen Falls**, over a series of waterfalls leading to the floor of a deeper glacial trough called the **Nant Ffrancon**. Here river processes have created features that overlie the glacial features from a pervious era. The **Nant Ffrancon** used to have a ribbon lake in its base. Over the millennia this has been filled in by deposits of alluvium (river sediments) creating a very flat valley floor. The Nant Ffrancon falls just 20 metres in height over 5km.

▲ fig.68 **The Nant Ffrancon valley, a glacial trough**

On leaving the Nant Ffrancon, the Afon Ogwen flows though the village of **Bethesda**. This village used to provide most of the workers for the nearby **Penrhyn slate quarry.** The quarry is still operational and its immense spoil heaps dominate the western banks of the Afon Ogwen near Bethesda.

On leaving Bethesda, the river continues toward the sea. It experiences a increase in gradient as it leaves the glacial valley and flows across the glaciers former outwash plain. Finally, the river enters the **Irish Sea** at the **Bangor Flats**. As the tidal range on this coast is very high the river can flow for an extra 2km at low tide, out across the mud flats.

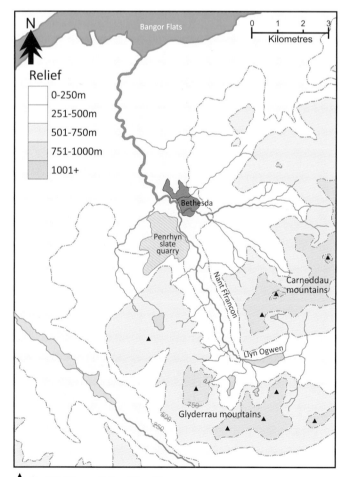

N

Bangor Flats

0 1 2 3
Kilometres

Relief

	0-250m
	251-500m
	501-750m
	751-1000m
	1001+

Bethesda

Penrhyn slate quarry

Nant Ffrancon

Carneddau mountains

Llyn Ogwen

Glyderrau mountains

▲ fig.67 **Map of the Afon Ogwen**

Landscapes are dynamic and differ depending on their geology, climate and human activity.

CASE STUDY

1. Just a few hundred metres from the source at 750m above sea level, the Afon Ogwen flows into a corrie tarn called **Ffynnon Loer.**

2. Having fallen 450m in just 2km, the river enters **Llyn Ogwen**, a glacial ribbon lake at the western end of the Ogwen valley.

3. Leaving Llyn Ogwen, the river plunges 100m down the **Ogwen Falls,** a series of cascades onto the floor of the **Nant Ffrancon.**

4. Leaving the Nant Ffrancon, the river flows past the slate wastes of the **Penrhyn Quarry** and through the village of **Bethesda.**

5. On leaving Bethesda, the river flows north, making a sharp turn west through dense woodland after the **Halfway Bridge.**

6. Finally, after 20km the river reaches its mouth where, at low tide, it flows out across the **Bangor Flats**, towards the **Irish Sea**.

fig.69 **Ffynnon Loer** fig.70 **Llyn Ogwen** fig.71 **Ogwen Falls** fig.72 **Bridge at Bethesda** fig.73 **Halfway Bridge** fig.74 **Bangor Flats**

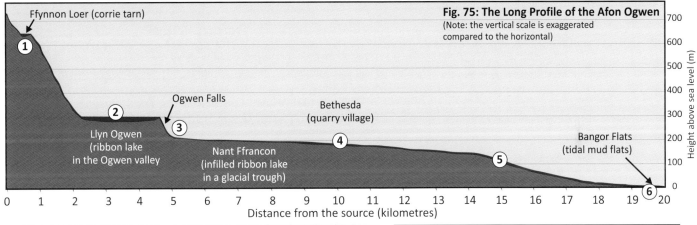

Fig. 75: The Long Profile of the Afon Ogwen
(Note: the vertical scale is exaggerated compared to the horizontal)

Ffynnon Loer (corrie tarn)

Ogwen Falls

Bethesda
(quarry village)

Llyn Ogwen
(ribbon lake
in the Ogwen valley

Nant Ffrancon
(infilled ribbon lake
in a glacial trough)

Bangor Flats
(tidal mud flats)

Height above sea level (m)

Distance from the source (kilometres)

A geological history of the Ogwen valley.

The river valley of the **Afon Ogwen** has not only been affected by glaciation. There is also a wide variety of underlying rock types as well as complex geological boundaries and faults between the differnt rocks.

Most of the rocks found in the Ogwen valley date form the Ordovician period around **400 million years ago**. During this period much of north Wales was **below sea level** and experienced **significant volcanic activity**. At times volcanic eruptions pushed the land upwards. At other times the land collapsed in a volcanic feature called a caldera.

This complex geological history is the reason why there are both **sedimentary, igneous and metamorphic rocks found closely together**. There are shallow water **marine sedimentary rocks** such as sandstones, and mudstones containing numerous fossils of brachiopods. This is a shelled marine creature whose fossils can also be found in the limestone of the **Great Orme**, near Llandudno (see page 27).

Inter-spaced between these layers of sediments are **igneous rocks**. Some are extrusive, such as **tuffs** which formed from ash flows that settled onto the sea bed. There are **pillow lavas** that were extruded directly into the sea as liquid rock during volcanic eruptions. There are also intrusive igneous rocks such as **granite.** This rock formed and cooled deep beneath the surface and has only been subsequently exposed by erosion.

Finally, there are **metamorphic slates**. Vast spoil heaps of slate waste dominate the western valley sides above the town of Bethesda and the **Penrhyn slate quarry**. These slates were originally deep-water mudstones deposited on the seabed around **1,500 metres** below the sea's surface. The **heat and pressure** associated with subsequent volcanic activity turned these mudstones into **slate**.

fig.76 **Was Snowdonia once like today's Kilauea in Hawaii?**

Darwin's field trip

fig.77 **Charles Darwin**

In **1831**, the same year that he joined the famous expedition onboard *The Beagle*, Charles Darwin visited the Ogwen Valley and Cwm Idwal for a geology field trip. When he found brachiopod and coral fossils in sedimentary rocks 300m above sea level, Darwin realised that these rocks must have been **formed on the sea bed and then raised up by forces within the Earth's crust**.

In 1842 he returned to the area to study the **features of glaciation**. These features we now take for granted as a product of glaciers from a much colder period of time. Darwin's insights into these geological features helped shape some of the thinking behind his famous work on the *Origin of the Species.*

25

Landscapes are dynamic and differ depending on their geology, climate and human activity.

Ogwen: past and present

10,000 years ago the Ogwen valley was under deep ice cover. **2,000 years ago** the Romans mined the area for slate and other minerals. **500 years ago** Welsh subsistence farmers raised hardy 'Welsh Black' cattle on the hillsides. **By the 19th Century**, these cattle had mostly been replaced by sheep. Many of the farming families were now working in the local slate quarries. By the end of the 19th Century Penrhyn was the world's largest slate quarry employing almost **3000 workers**. Today just **200** staff remain but the quarry produces 500,000 tonnes of useable slate each year.

Tourism is now a major industry in the area, but wages are lower than in most industrial jobs. Thousands of walkers and climbers enjoy the **Glyderau** and **Carneddau** mountain ranges, east and west of the Nant Ffrancon. In 2013, **ZipWorld**, the longest zipwire in the Northern Hemisphere, opened in a disused part of the Penrhyn quarry. In 2017, the **Ynni Ogwen** scheme was completed generating hydroelectric power from the Afon Ogwen upstream of Bethesda.

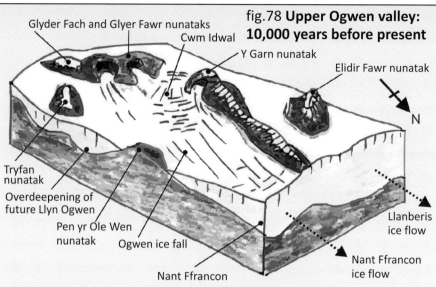

fig.78 **Upper Ogwen valley: 10,000 years before present**

Labels: Glyder Fach and Glyer Fawr nunataks; Cwm Idwal; Y Garn nunatak; Elidir Fawr nunatak; N; Tryfan nunatak; Overdeepening of future Llyn Ogwen; Pen yr Ole Wen nunatak; Ogwen ice fall; Nant Ffrancon; Llanberis ice flow; Nant Ffrancon ice flow

The diagram shows how the **upper Ogwen valley** may have appeared at the end of the last glacial, but before all the mountain glaciers had fully melted. The mountains over 900 metres in height stood above the ice, as **nunataks**. Today these mountains are covered with layers of **boulder scree** and huge slabs of rock, frost-shattered during this glaciation. The ice carved out the glacial trough now followed by the Afon Ogwen.

▼ fig.79 **Ordnance Survey map, upper course of Agfon Ogwen, 1:25,000**

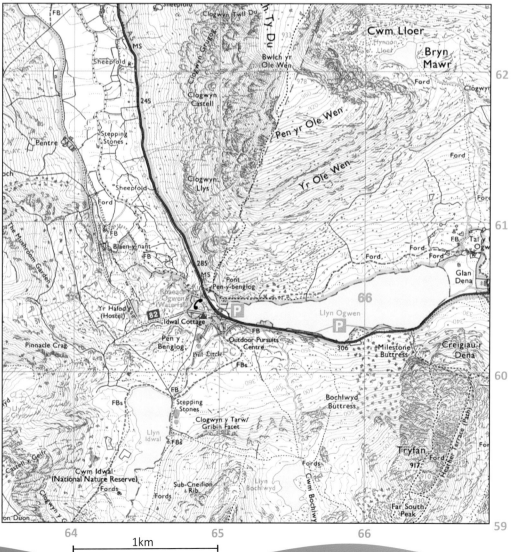

1km

1. What is the six-figure grid reference for the source of the Afon Ogwen, north east of **Ffynon Lloer**? (1)

2. What is the height of **Pen yr Ole Wen** to the west of Cwm Lloer. (1)

3. What geographical feature is **Cwm Lloer?** (1)

4. How many metres from east to west is **Llyn Ogwen**? (1)

5. What is the **widest part of Llyn Ogwen** in metres? (1)

6. What is the **six-figure grid reference of the Idwal Cottage** Youth Hostel? (1)

7. At approximately what **height above sea level is Llyn Ogwen** found? (1)

8. How **wide is the flat valley floor of the Nant Ffrancon** at the stepping stones found at GR 642 615? (1)

9. With reference to the OS map, **describe the long-profile of the Afon Ogwen** from its source to the stepping stones at GR 642 615. (6)

Landscapes are dynamic and differ depending on their geology, climate and human activity.

CASE STUDY

North Wales Coast Case Study: Great Orme to Talacre

The eastern section of the **North Wales coast** runs for 43km from the estuary of the River **Conwy and the Great Orme**, in the west, to **Talacre and the River Dee**, in the east. This coast of the **Irish Sea** exhibits significant changes in geology. It also has a rich human history.

This coastline had a relatively military presence during the Roman occupation of Britain. Even today the people of Abergele exhibit a high percentage of chromosomes linked to those Roman soldiers. During medieval times, the coast became host to two new castles: **Conwy** and **Rhuddlan**. These castles, still standing today, were built by Edward 1st during his conquest of Wales.

Today, the coastline is known mostly for its seaside resorts. **Rhyll** and **Prestatyn** are at the eastern end while **Llandudno**, is at the western end. Llandudno, the 'Queen of Welsh resorts' sits on the Creuddyn peninsula, across the river from the town and castle at Conwy.

Off the coastline are banks of wind turbines at the **North Hoyle, Rhyl Flats** and **Gwynt y Mor** wind farms. These three offshore wind farms, with a combined **total of 215 turbines**, can produce green electricity for an estimated **680,000 homes** (see page 79 for more on wind power).

Geology plays a significant role in how waves have shaped the coastline. The **Great Orme** marks the western edge of this stretch of coastline. The Orme is a massive outcrop of limestone. Once an island, the Orme was connected to the mainland by sediments deposited at the mouth of the **Afon Conwy** to create a **tombolo**, on which **Llandudno** is built.

Beach material, trapped between the Great Orme and the **Little Orme** (three kilometres to the east) has created the wide sweeping beach of **Llandudno Bay**.

East of the Little Orme, longshore drift has acted to **move sediments eastwards** towards **Talacre** and the **Dee Estuary**. Significant efforts have ben made to manage coastal erosion, as both the **North Wales Mainline** railway and the **North Wales Expressway** run close to the shore.

To the east of **Abergele** and the mouth of the **Afon Clwyd**, the coastline becomes depositional. Wide sandy beaches are exposed at low tide. This area has long been assdociated with **holiday resorts**, which are popular with holiday makers from Liverpool and Merseyside.

The **Point of Ayr Lighthouse** at Talacre beach marks the eastern end of this stretch of coastline. The lighthouse closed in 1884.

fig.80 Llandudno Bay from the Great Orme

Welcome to Llandudno

Llandudno is the largest seaside resort in Wales. It grew between 1867 and 1887 after the construction of the North Wales railway line, which stops at **Llandudno Junction**.

Llandudno Bay is faced by **The Parade,** impressive Victorian terraces painted in distinctive pastel colours.

fig.81 Llandudno Lifeboat

Llandudno is unique in the United Kingdom in that its **lifeboat** station is located inland. This allows the lifeboat to launch equally quickly from either the West Shore or the North Shore, depending on where it is needed.

Fig.82 **West Shore**

Fig.83 **Penrhyn Bay**

fig.84 **Rhos-on-Sea pier**

fig.85 **Rhyl harbour bridge**

fig.86 **Prestatyn sea wall**

fig.87 **Talacre lighthouse**

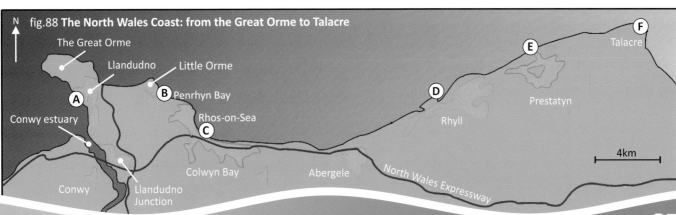
fig.88 **The North Wales Coast: from the Great Orme to Talacre**

N

The Great Orme
Llandudno — Little Orme
A
B Penrhyn Bay
Conwy estuary
Rhos-on-Sea
C
Colwyn Bay
Conwy   Llandudno Junction
Abergele
North Wales Expressway
D
Rhyll
E
Prestatyn
F
Talacre
4km

27

Landscapes are dynamic and differ depending on their geology, climate and human activity.

How is the North Wales Coast managed?

Every section of coastline in Britain is managed in some way. The North Wales coast is managed as part of an overall 'shoreline management plan' for the stretch of coastline that runs from the Great Ormes Head all the way to the Solway Firth on the Scottish border. This is known as **Cell 11**. The North Wales coast is the western section of one part of the coastline known as **'sub-cell' 11a**.

The most recent **Shoreline Management Plan** (SMP) was published in 2010. The plan is drawn up in consultation with local authorities, the Environment Agency, conservation bodies, such as English Heritage, and the Welsh government.

The plan looks at current management strategies, current and future issues and threats. It outlines a strategy and plans for future management.

The **North Wales coast is heavily**

fig.89 **Tetrapod sea defences**

managed. This is because, as the SMP points out, *"over the last 200 years, the construction of a mixture of seawalls, revetments, groynes and flood embankments along the majority of the North Wales coast has prevented shoreline erosion and managed flood risk to*

fig.90 **Sea wall and revetment, Prestatyn**

coastal towns (including Llandudno, Rhos-on-Sea, Colwyn Bay, Towyn, Rhyl and Prestatyn), tourism assets and infrastructure."

These towns and the associated transport infrastructure **need protecting from storm damage** and **coastal erosion**.

Between Colwyn Bay and Abergele, both train tracks and main roads run close to the coastline. Severe damage to this coastal infrastructure would severely disrupt transport across the region. The high cost of defending this coastline is considered worthwhile compared to the costs of allowing erosional damage and storm flooding.

However, defences can cause problems. Referring to the existing sea defences, the SMP states that, *"these structures have also led to a lowering of beach levels, erosion of dunes and the*

How does the geology affect the North Wales Coast?

The North Wales coast displays a wide variety of geology, from the **sedimentary limestones** of the Great Orme and Little Orme to **sandstones and coal measures**.

Around Conwy and Llandudno, **volcanic activity has also added complexity** to the geology. This complexity has, in turn, affected rates of coastal erosion, helping to create bays and headlands in the west and long sandy beaches in the east.

The **dolomite limestone** of the Great Orme is rich in **copper ores** and a Bronze Age mine operated on the site up to 1,500 years BC.

Today, the Great Orme is used for **farming and recreation**. Further along the coast at **Llanddulas**, between Colwyn Bay and Abergele, **Raynes Quarry** extracts limestone. This is transported by conveyor belt over the A55 Expressway to a jetty where it is loaded onto ships. Saint Margaret's **'Marble Church'** at

Bodelwyddan is built from this same high quality limestone.

Vast qualities of sediment, eroded from the **sandstone Clywddian Hills**, and transported by the Clywdd and Dee rivers, has produced the deep sands which make up the beaches of the eastern coast.

Coal was mined from the 11th Century at Mostyn, near Talacre. The nearby **Point of Ayr Colliery** finally closed in 1996, ending over 700 years of coal mining in the area.

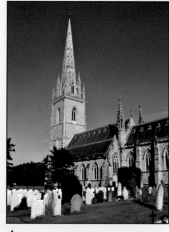

▲fig.91 **The Marble Chrurch**

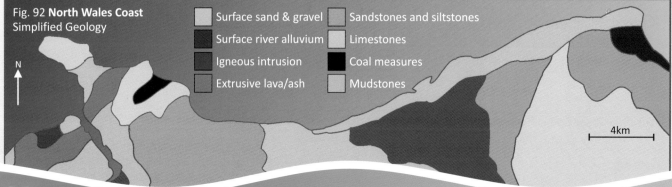

Fig. 92 **North Wales Coast**
Simplified Geology

N

- ☐ Surface sand & gravel
- ■ Surface river alluvium
- ▨ Igneous intrusion
- ☐ Extrusive lava/ash
- ▨ Sandstones and siltstones
- ☐ Limestones
- ■ Coal measures
- ☐ Mudstones

4km

28

Landscapes are dynamic and differ depending on their geology, climate and human activity.

need for beach management."

In some instances shoreline management plans may suggest a change in management strategies.

"Managed realignment was considered as an alternative policy at a number of locations along the North Wales coast." The SMP continues, *"However, this was rejected due to the need to construct longer lengths of defence, limited realignment space available due to infrastructure and land levels, and the limited potential to create habitats in the longer term as sea levels rise. Therefore there is strong justification to continue to manage erosion and flooding risks for most of this frontage over the next century by maintaining defences on their current alignment. However, this is likely to result in increasing beach loss."*

Coastal strategies

There are numerous strategies being used to protect the North Wales coast. **Wooden groynes** and **rock armour 'fish tail' groynes** are used to slow longshore drift along the coast. **Sea walls** prevent

fig.93 **'Fish-tail' groyne at Prestatyn**

coastal flooding from Llandudno to Prestatyn.

Interlocking **concrete tetrapods** defend the coast east of Colwyn Bay. These interlocking blocks are numbered and photographed so that movement in their location can be mapped and potential future problems avoided.

Beach nourishment has been used to replenish the beach at Llandudno. Excess beach material from the West Shore was moved and dumped onto the North Shore to widen the beach.

However, coastal protection is expensive. In 2014 Conwy Council spent around £5 million repairing damage caused by the 2013/14 winter storms.

Thinking it through

1. State the six-figure grid reference for the end of **Llandudno Pier**. (1)

2. What **leisure activity** is found at grid reference **775 808**? (1)

3. What **coastal defence** is found at grid reference **771 806**? (1)

4. What is the length, in kilometres, of the beach in **Ormes Bay/Llandudno Bay?** (1)

5. Describe the **height and relief** of the **Great Orme**. (3)

6. Describe some of the **tourist attractions** available for visitors to the Great Orme. (3)

7. Using evidence on the map, suggest the possible **land use** at **782 814.** (1)

8. What is the **actual distance** travelling on the A546 from the roundabout at **779 811** to **791 821**? (1)

9. The **tourist information** at **782 823** is found in which public building? (1)

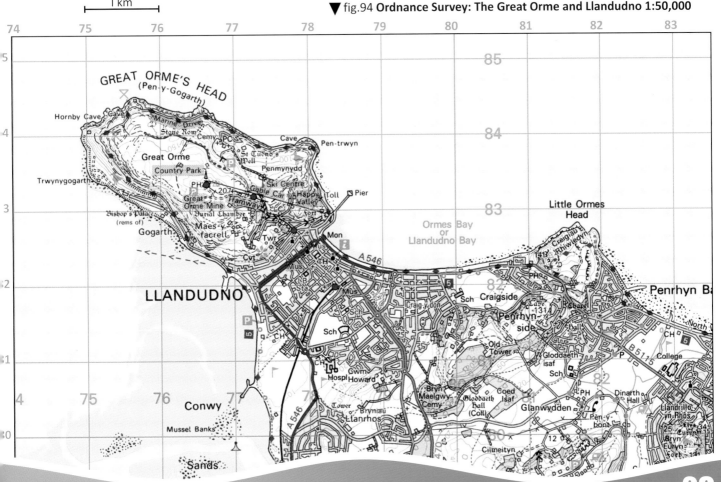

▼ fig.94 **Ordnance Survey: The Great Orme and Llandudno 1:50,000**

I km

29

Landscapes are dynamic and differ depending on their geology, climate and human activity.

fig.95 **The Little Orme and Llandudno Bay**

Thinking it through

1. Describe the **location of the Afon Ogwen** and its valley. (2)

2. Explain how the **human management of the Afon Ogwen** river basin has helped shape its current appearance. (6)

3. Describe some of the **land uses** which take place in a river valley drainage basin you have studied. (4)

4. Assess the relative importance of **erosion and deposition** in creating the different features of the Afon Ogwen valley. (8)

5. Describe the main **geomorphic processes operating** in the upper course of the Afon Ogwen. (4)

6. Describe the **orientation of a coastline** you have studied. (2)

7. Describe the **cause and effect of longshore drift** along a coastline you have studied. (6)

8. Describe, and give evidence for, **two geomorphic processes** operating along a coastline you have studied. (6)

9. With reference to a coastline you have studied, **describe how and why the coast is managed** at different places. (6)

10. With reference to a coast you have studied, assess the **relative importance of both erosion and deposition** in creating and shaping the features of that coastline. (8)

11. Describe **one method of coastal defence** that is used on a stretch of coastline you have studied. (3)

Your Revision checklist

You must make sure you are confident about the range of **landforms** found within the coastal landscape. So you need to be able to both **describe** (say what it looks like) and **explain their formation** (write about the processes needed, and stages that are involved, to create the feature). You must know about all of the following features: **headlands and bays**, (page 20-21) **caves, arches, stacks,** (page 21) **beaches** and **spits** (pages 22-23.)

You must also be clear about your **two case studies** - one of a **river valley** (pages 24-26) and another of a **coastline** (pages 27-29). In these case studies you need to be clear about their locations as well as geomorphic processes operating at different scales. You should be able to describe and explain, whether erosion or deposition are more significant in certain places.

You should know how these processes are influenced by **geology** and **climate**. You should be clear about the landforms and features associated with your case studies and how human activity, including **management**, works in combination with geomorphic processes to impact the landscape.

Top tips for exam success

GCSEs can be stressful but getting stressed is no help when it comes to exam success. The following are top tips for exam success:

⊙ **Create three zones for yourself.**
It's important to create a *study zone*; a *relaxation zone* and a *sleep zone*. Keep these areas distinct and make sure the study and sleep spaces are calm and uncluttered. Don't revise in bed or when watching the telly.

⊙ **Plan and use a revision timetable.**
Schedule time to study, relax and sleep. Break revision periods into manageable chunks. Don't do too much in one go. Don't do too little either.

⊙ **Take regular breaks.**
Break your study up into twenty minute chunks. You should not study for more than two hours without taking a break of about twenty minutes. These short breaks should be used to unwind, chat to friends, have a drink and eat a healthy snack. It's also important to take an extended break each day to really 'switch off' from studying.

⊙ **Eat a healthy diet and exercise.**
Eating healthy food and drinking at regular intervals throughout the day will maintain your energy levels and concentration. Avoid too much coffee, tea or 'energy' drinks, as the caffeine can make you feel agitated and stop you sleeping. Exercising regularly helps release adrenalin, clear your mind and reduce stress.

⊙ **Sleep well and make sure you sleep long enough**
Maintain a regular sleep pattern. Always aim to get at least eight hours sleep per night and try to fit in one hour of relaxation before you go to bed.

Landscapes are dynamic and differ depending on their geology, climate and human activity.

How is Britain connected to the rest of the world?

The United Kingdom is connected to the rest of the world through complex inter-relationships of **trade, transnational organisations and military alliances**. There are also millions of **personal connections**, between family members and through work connections and friendships.

These connections are in a constant state of change. Governments change and new businesses emerge. Changing patterns of **migration** create new connections within the global economy.

Making global connections is easier today as **long-distance travel** is much faster with trains and airlines moving millions of people around the world every hour. Trade has expanded as the cost and time needed to ship goods around the world has fallen.

A few hundred years ago most people would be unlikely to travel more than a few tens of miles from their place of birth; perhaps to the nearest town or city.

Today millions of young people think nothing of moving to a new town or city to start a university education. Millions more move for work, in search of a better life or safety from wars or natural disasters.

As the world becomes **more integrated**, by both travel and trade, organisations have developed with the aim of managing the relationships between different countries. These organisations are not always successful. Wars and conflicts are more common today than they were 100 years ago.

Very few countries can separate themselves off from the rest of the world. Britain, with its history of **colonial empire**, **large economy** and an active **government foreign policy**, is particularly well connected with many parts of the globe.

▲ fig.96 **Felixstowe port**

Britain has **110 ports and harbours**, vital for 95% of imports and exports worth billions of pounds each year. Felixstowe port handles 42% of Britain's containerised trade.

The 'International Community'

▲ fig.97
UK connections

The Commonwealth
United Nations
World Trade Organisation
European Court of Human Rights
International connections
International Criminal Court
NATO
Interpol

The European Union: what will 'Brexit' mean?

In a referendum on 23rd June 2016, Britain voted to leave the **European Union**. The UK has been a member since 1973. The debate split the country with 52% voting 'Leave' and 48% voting 'Remain.' The process of leaving the EU will take several years. You should keep yourself up to date with this process, that has been nicknamed "**Brexit**," and its implications for Britain's global role.

The United Kingdom - well connected to the rest of the world.

fig.98 **The Channel Tunnel**

The Channel Tunnel. Opened in 1994, the **Channel Tunnel** connects Britain with France. Running 50km under the English Channel from Folkestone to Calais, the tunnel carries passengers, cars and lorries on trains. The trains includes the high speed **Eurostar** services from **London St Pancras** to France and Belgium.

fig.99 **Heathrow Airport**

Airports. Britain has **24 international airports**. The busiest is **London Heathrow**, responsible for 75 million passenger journeys in 2015. Heathrow is the sixth busiest airport on the planet.

fig.100 **The Port of Dover**

Passenger Ports. The UK has **48 passenger ports**. Over half of these connect up the Scottish islands, while the rest connect Britain with European countries. The **Port of Dover**, just 34 km from France, is the world's busiest passenger port, carrying 16 million passengers and over 5 million vehicles every year.

KEY TERMS

Commonwealth: a voluntary international organisation of Britain's ex-colonies.

Economy: the total set of interactions between individuals, companies, the government and the rest of the world.

European Union: an economic and political union of 28 European countries.

Exports: Goods and services sold abroad.

Foreign Direct Investment: investments from overseas companies into another country.

Imports: Goods and services bought abroad.

International trade: The buying and selling of goods, services and raw materials between different countries.

NATO: Military alliance consisting of the United States, Canada, Turkey and 25 European nations.

United Nations: an international body, based in New York, representing all the nation states in the World, formed in 1945.

How is Britain connected to the world economy?

The **economy** of a country can be described as the entire network of producers, distributors, and consumers of **goods, services and raw materials**. Economies have a local, regional, national and international context.

The **'British economy'** describes how the people in the UK make their living on a daily basis through the entire range of jobs, occupations and lifestyles. **'Economy'** is a simple word for a **very complex set of interactions between millions of people, companies, layers of government and the rest of the world.**

A common way of describing an economy is by giving it a monetary value such as **GDP (Gross Domestic Product)**. This is an estimate of the value of goods, services and raw materials produced in a country each year.

To allow us to compare different countries with different currencies the GDP is usually converted into its value in United States Dollars.

In 2015 the UK economy was valued at **$US 2.849 trillion**. As the population size of countries varies greatly, the GDP is often divided by the population to give a figure per capita (per person). In 2015, the UK GDP was **$US44,700** per capita.

Sometimes this figure is adjusted for

fig.101 **City of London**

Purchasing Power Parity (PPP) which adjusts the dollar figure to take account of the cost of living and prices in a particular country. After converting for PPP, the UK GDP figure for 2015 fell to **US$42,200**.

Is there more to an economy than the raw data?

While **GDP figures per capita give a flavour of the size** of an economy, they do not tell you how the wealth of a country is actually divided. Did you earn $44,700 last year? Economists look for how income is divided or how much different groups consume. The **GINI Index** looks at wealth inequality. The lower the GINI figure the more equally distributed the nation's income. **Britain ranks 35th for equality** with a GINI score of 32.4. The poorest 10% of the UK population receive 1.7% of the nation's income. Meanwhile the richest 10% receive 31%. Scandinavian counties are more equal with lower GINI scores: Denmark (24.8) and Sweden (24.9).

Most unequal economies tend to be found in poorer countries where the rich elite is very much richer than the majority of the populations. South Africa has a GINI score of 62.5. here the richest 10% receive 51.7% of the income while the poorest 10% get just 1.2%.

GDP figures only show part of the story. They don't show the detail of how a country makes its money. **Britain has one of the largest economies in the world** (ranked 5th in 2015). It is one of the most **complex and internationally integrated** economies in the world. This is a result of both the size and history of British capitalism.

This is shown by the value of goods we import from abroad and the value of goods we export to sell abroad.

Britain plays a very significant role in the movement of money around the world. The

fig.102 World's largest economies in 2015

The Global League Table

Rank: Country	GDP ($US)
1: USA	17,917 billion
2: China	10,983 billion
3: Japan	4,123 billion
4: Germany	3,358 billion
5: United Kingdom	2,849 billion
6: France	2,422 billion
7: India	2,091 billion
8: Italy	1,816 billion
9: Brazil	1,773 billion
10: Canada	1,552 billion

City of London is one of the top three financial centres on the planet. Financial transactions amount to **$US 1.85 trillion every day**. Amazingly, there are more US Dollars bought and sold in London each day than in New York.

An analysis of the British economy needs to be broken down into **different sectors** to be able to compare it with other countries. Different countries will have different strengths and weaknesses in their economies.

While Germany gets 30% of its GDP from manufacturing industry and South Korea gets 38%, the figure for Britain is just 19.7%. Farming in Britain amounts to just 0.6% of GDP, whereas it is nearly 12% of GDP in Romania or 41% in Ethiopia.

▼ fig.103 **Britain's imports in 2015 were worth US$645 billion**

Western Europe 37%

Eastern Asia 12%

Rest of Asia 8%

North America 11%

Northern Europe 11%

0.75%

South and Eastern Europe 14%

3.25%

Africa 3%

■ South America ■ Oceania

KEY TERMS

Advanced Countries (ACs): Countries classified by the International Monetary Fund as having well-developed financial markets, diversified economic structures and rapidly growing service sectors.

GDP: Gross domestic product: the total value of goods, services and raw materials produced in a country each year.

GINI Index: a statistical method used to represent the income distribution of a nation's residents, and is most commonly used as a measure of inequality.

Purchasing Power Parity: a statistical method of adjusting the GDP of a country to take into account exchange rate and the relative cost of goods and services.

CHINA SHIPPING LINE

What does the United Kingdom import and export?

Looking at what a country imports and exports can tell geographers a lot about its economy. Poorer countries tend to export lower value, agricultural goods and import more expensive, manufactured goods. Britain has one of the **most complex and internationally integrated economies** in the world.

As we can see from figure 105, Britain imports and exports lots of the same products. This may seem confusing until we look a little deeper at exactly what is being bought and sold, and who is doing the importing and exporting.

Almost half of all the cars the UK imports are made in Germany such as BMWs, Volkswagens and Mercedes. However, only 6% of the cars Britain sells abroad are sent to Germany.

Britain imports more goods than are sold abroad. This is called the **balance of trade deficit**. In recent years Britain has had a significant balance of trade deficit. Many people believe is a weakness in the UK economy. Others believe that Britain's stre ngth in financial services, such as banking, makes up for this weakness.

In the aftermath of Britain's decision to **leave the EU**, there will be significant interest in how Britain renegotiates its **trade relationship** with the rest of the EU

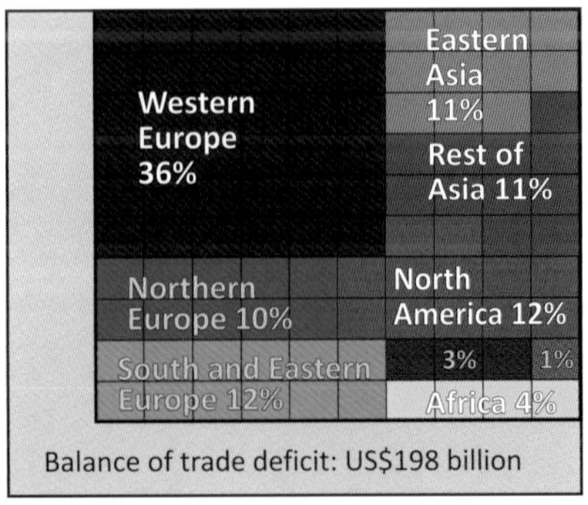

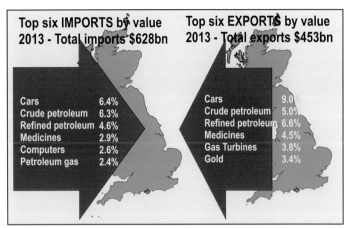

▲ Fig.105 **Britain's imports and exports in 2013**
▼ Fig.106 **Container ship leaving Felixstowe port**

Western Europe 36%	Eastern Asia 11%
	Rest of Asia 11%
Northern Europe 10%	North America 12%
South and Eastern Europe 12%	3%	1%
	Africa 4%

Balance of trade deficit: US$198 billion

▲ fig.104 **Britain's exports worth US$447 billion in 2015.**

Imports to the UK

The UK is a large economy with lots of companies and individuals able to buy goods manufactured abroad.

✱ While we do import lots of food stuffs from tropical fruits to cereal grains, the value of these goods is not as high as the manufactured goods we buy.

✱ Lots of electronic goods and toys come from China, as they are cheaper to produce there than in the UK.

✱ Britains are able to buy expensive German (Audi, BMW, Mercedes) or Swedish (Volvo, Saab) cars, as well as more budget European cars (Wolkswagon, Citroen, Fiat, Seat, etc.)

✱ Petroleum products provide fuel and raw materials for our own industries.

Exports from the UK

While the UK has a smaller manufacturing base than Germany, the country does make products with a global demand.

✱ The UK's biggest export market is the USA, where UK-made luxury cars, such a Rolls Royce or Jaguar, sell well.

✱ Aeronautical exports are significant, with Roll Royce engines fitted to many planes.

✱ High quality North Sea crude oil is in high demand globally.

✱ In 2015, UK-processed gems, precious metals and coins were in high demand globally as investments.

Thinking it through

1. Distinguish between **imports** and **exports**. (2)

2. Using fig.105, what was Britains biggest export sector by value in 2013? (1)

3. What is meant by the term **advanced country**? (1)

4. What is meant by the letters **GDP**? (1)

5. Explain why **GDP figures** alone are not always sufficient to describe a nation's economy. (4)

6. Describe what is shown by the **GINI index**. (3)

7. With reference to figures 102 and 104, discuss why Britain leaving the free trade area of the EU, after the 'Brexit' vote, may impact on Britain's **trading patterns.** (6)

8. "Britain's GDP hides an unequal society." Discuss to what extent **you agree** with this statement. (6)

9. "Britain's economy is **fully integrated** in the global economy." Discuss this statement. (6)

10. Explain why Britain imports so many **goods from China,** despite it being so far away. (4)

11. When describing and comparing the economies of different countries why is the concept of **purchasing power parity** (PPP) useful? (4)

12. With reference to figures 102 and 103, what percentage of **UK trade took place European countries** in 2015? (4)

How is the United Kingdom geographically diverse?

One of the things that makes the UK so interesting is its diversity. Whether that is the **landscape diversity**, looked at in Section 1.1 or the **economic, social and cultural diversity**, which we will look at in this section.

We have already seen (Section 1.2.1) that Britain has a **diverse economy** and wealth is divided **unequally** amongst all its citizens .

As a nation of many immigrants, we have a **rich cultural heritage**. Each new wave of migrants brings with them new additions to the UK's cultural tapestry.

Geographers study the **spatial patterns** of the physical and human worlds. We can see significant local, regional and national variations in a range of the human features of the United Kingdom. **Employment, average incomes, educational attainment, life expectancy, ethnicity** and even access to **broadband internet** all show great variations.

These patterns change in response to **changes in the economy** as well as internal and external migration.

▲ Fig.107 **Nissan car factory, Sunderland**

UK employment patterns

⊙ Patterns of employment are constantly changing as economies develop. The total number of people in work has increased in the UK but there have been significant **changes in the structure and patterns of employment** over the last 25-30 years.

⊙ Manufacturing (secondary sector) jobs have declined, to be replaced by jobs in the service (tertiary) sector.

⊙ New jobs in the so-called **creative industries and information technology** (the quaternary sector) have emerged as technology advances. Many Hollywood blockbusters, such as Star Wars, rely on British film studios for the special effects.

⊙ Many people now work more **'flexible' hours** rather than the traditional 9am to 5pm. Sometimes this is by choice but in many cases the flexibility is demanded by the employer.

⊙ There has been an increase in **part-time employment** and the numbers of people defined as self-employed.

⊙ Since the 'financial crisis' of 2008/9 there has been **decline in those employed by the public sector.**

⊙ There has been an **increase in the total number of women employed** in both part-time and full-time work.

▲ Fig.108 **Storm Troopers - a quaternary job?**

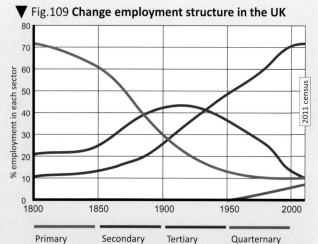

▼ Fig.109 **Change employment structure in the UK**

% employment in each sector

2011 census

1800   1850   1900   1950   2000

Primary   Secondary   Tertiary   Quaternary

✶ Statistics can be confusing as different organisations present their statistics in different ways. The graph above divides employment into 4 categories. In this model extractive industries such a quarrying are classified as primary industries. However, In the Office of National Statistics model (fig.109) extractive industries are classified as production and so are grouped with manufacturing (secondary) jobs. In fig.109, farming, forestry and construction are grouped in 'other' and 'services' include those in the quaternary sector.

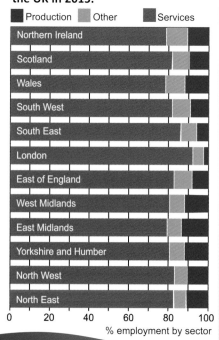

▼ Fig.110 **Employment by sector in the UK in 2015.**

■ Production   ■ Other   ■ Services

Northern Ireland
Scotland
Wales
South West
South East
London
East of England
West Midlands
East Midlands
Yorkshire and Humber
North West
North East

0   20   40   60   80   100
% employment by sector

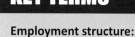

KEY TERMS

Employment structure: the types of jobs performed in any economy.

Primary sector: jobs in farming, fishing and raw material extraction.

Quaternary sector: jobs in the 'knowledge-based' creative and information technology.

Secondary sector: jobs in manufacturing industries.

Tertiary sector: jobs which provides a service to another person, company or society.

Average income

The average median family income in the UK in 2015 is **£25,600** per year. However, when it comes to averages, they can be particularly confusing when referring to income. **The mean annual income is several thousand pounds higher than the median**. This is because there are a minority of people who are **very wealthy** in Britain.

In fact, there are around **720,000 millionaires** in Britain (1 in 65 of the population.) Their wealth, and the incomes of people like top football players and company directors, distort the overall picture. Directors of the top 100 FTSE companies earn on average 150 times the salaries of their workers. In other words, they earn in under three days what their workers earn in one whole year.

Britain has a minimum wage which, in theory, prevents employers paying wages which are too low. Most new jobs, created in the last few years, pay at or close to the minimum wage. Three quarters of these jobs pay less than £16,000 per year.

Disposable income measures the money people have to live on once they have paid their taxes, pension contributions and rent or mortgage.

▲ Fig.109 **Manchester City players earned £194 million in 2015-16**

While the **average family disposable income is around £17,500** per year, there are large variations across Britain, within regions and between different parts of the same town or city.

Northern Ireland has the smallest range between average family disposable incomes. The North of the region is lowest at around £13,000 per year, while Outer Belfast averages just over £15,000.

Meanwhile **London shows the greatest disparity in disposable income.** The figure in Barking and Dagenham is around £17,000 per family per year but bthis rises to £43,500 in affluent Westminster.

In the North West, 'leafy' Cheshire averages £19,000 while Blackburn and Darwen families struggle by on just over £12,000 per year.

Life expectancy

Life expectancy is a measure of the average number of years a person may expect to live if born at certain time. Life expectancy has been rising steadily for over a century. In fact, during the 20th Century, for every year that passed life average expectancy rose by three months.

Clean water, healthy food, vaccinations, access to anti-biotic medicines and lifestyle are the key factors in rising life expectancy. The decline in dangerous manual professions such as coal mining has also played a role in improved life spans.

In the UK average life expectancy is now 81 years. That's 5 years longer than in 1990.

However, **life expectancy is not equal.** Women tend to live longer than men. A baby girl born today in Manchester could be expected to live to the age of 79.9 years while a boy could expect 75.8 years of life. This is almost **8 years less than for a child born in London's Kensington and Chelsea**, where boys and girls can expect to live to 83.3 and 86.4 year respectively.

The two regions with the lowest average life expectancy are Scotland (79.1 years) and North Ireland (79.6 years).

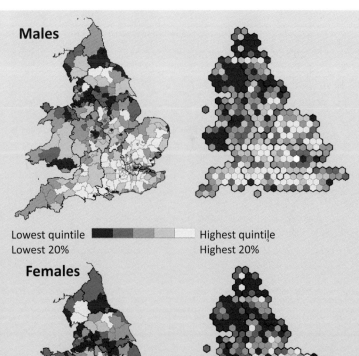

Males

Lowest quintile / Lowest 20% — Highest quintile / Highest 20%

Females

Fig.110 **Life expectancy in England and Wales, 2012-14**

The graphic above shows the local authority areas (shown on the map and represented by a hexagon) with life expectancy divided into five quintiles. Each quintile contains 69 authorities.

Source: Office of National Statistics, *Life Expectancy at Birth and at Age 65 by Local Areas in England and Wales, ONS, 4th November 2015.*
Reproduced under open government license, v.3.0

English Region	Average life expectancy (years)	
	♂	♀
North East	78	81.7
North West	78.1	81.9
Yorkshire/Humber	78.7	82.4
East Midlands	79.4	83
West Midlands	78.9	82.9
East	80.4	83.8
London	80.3	84.2
South East	80.5	84
South West	80.2	83.9

▲ Fig.111 **Life expectancy in the English regions, 2012-14**

The UK is a diverse and unequal society which has geographical patterns.

Educational attainment

There are many ways to measure the success of education within any country and to look for patterns. Until recently the government used the percentage of students who attained 5 A*-C grades at GCSE as their benchmark.

This will change from 2016 to the Progress 8 indicator. You should be able to obtain data on Progress 8 from the website of the Office of National Statistics.

In 2015, across England 68.8 % of students entered for GCSEs attained 5 or more A*-C grades. The **best performing authority was the Scilly Isles** and the **least successful authority was Knowsley** in Merseyside.

London was the best performing region, with outer London doing slightly better then Inner London.

There are great variations within regions. While just 45.5% of students achieved the 5 good grades in Knowsley, that figure rose to 78% in Trafford. Here schools still use tests age 11 to choose their pupils.

In many cases there is a clear link between poverty and educational attainment. However, there are many factors that can affect how well a student does at school. Geographers can look for patterns which can help explain differences, but **there is no simple geographical link between attainment and location.**

Tower Hamlets in east London is one of the poorer council areas in London but in 2015 was one of the best performing authority areas in Inner London. Its students achieved above the London average of 70.1% 5 A*-C grades.

▼ Fig.114 **Educational attainment by region, 2015, for students attaining 5A*-C grades at GCSE**

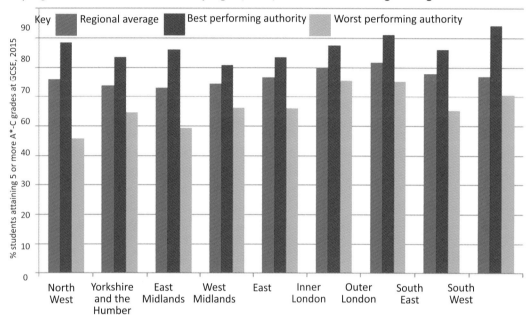

Access to broadband

Access to fast-speed broadband is considered by the government to be of particular importance. Large sums of money has been spent trying to improve access to broadband. **Speeds greater the 30Mbps were available to around 90% of the population by the end of 2015.**

Private companies, such as Virgin and BT, have invested heavily ensuring fast broadband connections in London and other major cities.

However, where population densities are low, such as the remote valleys of Wales or the Highlands of Scotland, there is **little incentive for private companies to install the expensive infrastructure** for super-fast broadband. It is here that government subsidies have been essential.

Despite large-scale coverage there are still pockets low availability. Looking at the broadband map of East Anglia (fig.115) you can see high speeds in the cities, such Norwich and Ipswich, but slower speeds in more rural villages. Quite **a few areas have very low broadband speeds where population densities are also low**.

▼ fig.115 **Broadband speeds in East Anglia, 2015**

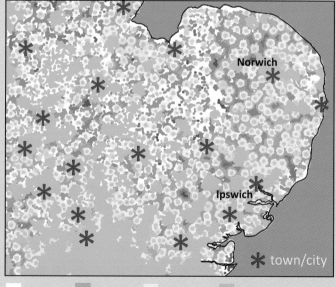

| no access | 0-4Mbps | 4-16Mbps | 16 and above Mbps |

Check out current broadband access and speeds at
http://maps.thinkbroadband.com/

The UK is a diverse and unequal society which has geographical patterns.

Ethnicity

Ethnicity is a simple term to describe a complex set of human relationships. Ethnicity is based on a set of shared characteristics, from national and religious groupings, through to historical, cultural and inherited characteristics. **Britain today is a multi-ethnic, and multi-cultural society**. As a nation of immigrants our society is a melting pot of different people.

A quick look at our common language, English, will show that it is composed of several other languages: Latin-based Norman French mixed with Norse and Germanic tongues, plus the subsequent addition of words and concepts from languages as diverse as Arabic, Turkish and languages from the Indian sub-continent.

The most ethnically-mixed populations in Britain are found in the large cities, with London being the most ethnically diverse city in the UK. The increase in the scale of migration in the last century has created an ever-changing mix of people. Most areas of Britain are now multi-ethnic, although **the majority 'white British' ethnic group makes up over 80% of the population.**

However, in London this figure falls to around 45%. Britain's cities have high concentrations of people who themselves, their parents, or even their great grandparents, may have moved to Britain in the last 100 years.

Some places become identified with people with a certain ethnicity. For example, part of Tower Hamlets or

	Other ethnic groups	Black, African, Black-British	Asian-British Asian	Mixed, multiple ethnicity	White
England and Wales	1	3.3	7.5	2.2	86.3
North East	0.4	0.5	2.9	0.9	95.3
North West	0.6	1.4	6.2	1.6	90.2
Yorkshire and the Humber	0.8	1.5	7.3	1.6	88.8
East Midlands	0.6	1.8	6.5	1.9	89.3
West Midlands	0.9	3.3	10.8	2.4	82.7
East of England	0.5	2	4.8	1.9	90.8
London	3.4	13.3	18.5	5	59.8
South East	0.6	1.6	5.2	1.9	90.7
South West	0.3	0.9	2	1.4	95.4
Wales	0.5	0.6	2.3	1	95.6

▲ Fig.116 **Ethnicity across the English and Welsh regions, 2011.**

Oldham are associated with people who have a Bangladeshi origin. Moss Side in Manchester has a high number of people of Somali origin.

However, in the most ethnically-diverse city outside London, Birmingham, 80% of the population identify themselves 'white'.

Ethnicity has a significant impact on other factors such as economic activity, family income and educational attainment. These relationships are as **complex as the concept of ethnicity itself.**

Attempts to find simple explanations for the differences between ethnic groups often rely on **negative stereotypes** and can lead to conflict within society.

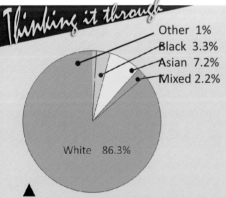

Other 1%
Black 3.3%
Asian 7.2%
Mixed 2.2%
White 86.3%

▲ Fig.117 **Ethnicity in England and Wales, 2011**

1. What is meant by the term **ethnicity** (1)

2. Using examples, describe what is meant by the term **'ethnic minority.'** (2)

3. With reference to figure 117, describe the **ethnic diversity** of the United Kingdom. (3)

4. With reference to figure 116, compare the **ethnic composition** of London's population with that of Wales. (3)

5. Suggest reasons why people of **similar ethnic minority groups** may be found living close together, especially in inner cities. (4)

6. Suggest reasons why London has the highest percentage of **non-white ethnic groups** in the UK. (3)

7. With reference to figure 109, (p34) describe the changes in Britain's **employment structure** between 1901 and 2011. (3)

8. With reference to figure 110, which regions of the UK employ the highest and the lowest percentages of their workforce in **production jobs**? (3)

9. What is meant by the term **quaternary industries**? (1)

10. Suggest reasons to explain why **life expectancy** is higher in London than in Greater Manchester. (3)

11. With reference to Figure 111, (p35) describe the **general pattern of life expectancy** for England and wales in 2011. (4)

12. With reference to Figure 114 (p36), which region of the UK shows the greatest variation in **educational attainment**? (2)

Immigration: a source of conflict

Immigration has often been a source of contention and social conflict within Britain. Some people claim that immigrants come to Britain to 'claim benefits' while others blame immigrants for 'taking British jobs.' Many others, however, celebrate the diversity and cultural richness that migrant communities bring to this country.

Economically, **migrants tend to put more into a country**, in terms of the taxes they pay, than they take out in the form of services. This is because migrants are often young and healthy, provide necessary skills and are usually prepared to work long hours to make their new life a success.

Some migrants such as **asylum seekers are not allowed to work** until their claims for refugee status have been processed. This can lead to others seeing them as 'lazy' when, in reality, they really want to work.

▼ Fig.118 **Refugees in camp in Calais, 2016**

The UK is a diverse and unequal society which has geographical patterns.

How do patterns of development change in the UK?

The United Kingdom is a diverse country with diverse geographical patterns. This is equally true when we look at the economic geography of the country. In 2016 Britain was the **5th largest economy in the world**, but that **economic activity wasn't spread evenly** across the country.

Figures 119 and 120 shows the economic activity across the country by region. The map shows the GVA of each region. **GVA** refers to **Gross Value Added**. This is a measure of the value of goods and services produced in an area, industry or sector of an economy.

The areas with **high GVA are the areas where economic activity add the most value to the economy.** This is a purely economic figure and doesn't tell us how hard people are working or what they are doing, just the value that they add to the economy in monetary terms.

The maps shows us that the region adding least economic value is Wales and

the region producing most is London.

UK core and periphery

In geographical terms London can be described as the 'core' of the economy. Here economic activity is growing. This **draws in more investment and creates further jobs.** This then creates the demand for other services in the supply chain and the services for the growing workforce. The result is a **virtuous circle** of economic growth.

Wales and the North East can be referred to as the **'periphery.'** Here declining industry leads to a **loss of jobs and declining investment**. This leads to an out-migration of workers, especially those with desirable skills. As a result there is a decline in demand for local services leading to further economic contraction. This creates a **vicious cycle** of decline.

There are also **great variations within regions**. Geographers seek to explain the detail and well as the big picture.

▼ Fig.119 **Gross Value Added by region , 2014**

■	28,000 - 42,666
■	23,000 - 27,999
■	21,000 - 22,999
▨	19,000 - 20,999
▨	18,000 - 18,999
□	17,573 - 17-999

GVA per head (£)

source: ONS

Gross Value Added (GVA) is a measure of the increase in the value of the economy due to the production of goods and services. It is measured at current prices excluding taxes such as Value Added Tax. GVA plus taxes on products is equivalent to Gross Domestic Product (GDP).
National Average £24,616 per head

GVA by region - where is the wealth created?

An investigation of GVA by region begins to show up some of the disparities in the UK economy. **Only five areas have a GVA above the national average.** This is because the West Inner London region creates so much value that it distorts the whole UK picture.

At a smaller scale, Camden and the City of London have a GVA per capita of £298,529. Westminster has a GVA of £218,788. Together the GVA of these two areas, dependent on finance and banking, is twenty times greater then Angelsey, North Wales. Angelsey has a GVA of just £13,162 per person.

North East Scotland GVA is boosted by the value created in Aberdeen by the North Sea oil industry. In geographical terms, this type of area is known as a **resource frontier** where the growing economy is based on the exploitation of natural resources.

The GVA of the Gwent Valleys (the former coal mining heartland of South Wales), is second lowest in the UK at £13,479 per capita. This shows what can happen to an area, once rich in raw materials, when the resources run out or are deemed too expensive to exploit in a profitable way.

KEY TERMS

De-industrialisation: the process by with employment in heavy industry, such as ship building, is replaced by jobs in the service sector.

Development: the process by which the quality of life and the standard of living for the people of a region or country improves over time.

Economic core: the centre of a country's economy, typified by an vibrant economy, and influx of investment and growing population.

Economic periphery: a declining region of a country, often some distance from the core, typically with low levels of investment and an out-migration of workers.

Resource frontier: a recently growing region of a country's economy centred around raw materials, such as oil or minerals.

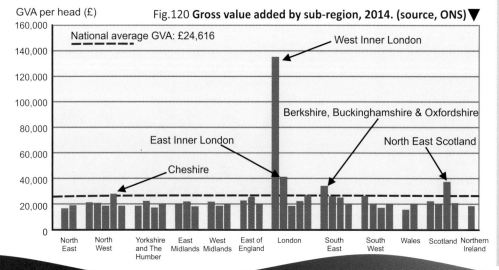

GVA per head (£)   Fig.120 **Gross value added by sub-region, 2014. (source, ONS)** ▼

National average GVA: £24,616

West Inner London
Berkshire, Buckinghamshire & Oxfordshire
East Inner London
North East Scotland
Cheshire

North East | North West | Yorkshire and The Humber | East Midlands | West Midlands | East of England | London | South East | South West | Wales | Scotland | Northern Ireland

There are different causes and consequences of development within the UK which has geographical patterns.

What factors affect economic development?

Geographical location

London grew as a result of its position as a crossing point over the River Thames. As **London** became the centre of political rule in Britain, it also became the **economic core.**

In the past, the Thames was a perfect access point to the country. London's dock brought in **goods from across the British Empire** and sent manufactured goods outwards across the globe.

London's docks on the Isle of Dogs have long since closed. They were too small for modern ships. However, London had become a **national and international economic centre**, drawing in people from across the country and the world.

As transport links have improved **more and more people are able to commute daily into London**, whilst living in pleasant rural or semi-rural locations.

Britain's membership of the European Union gave it access to the markets of northern Europe and other member states. Many of the imports and exports to and from these countries come through London and the South East, with its cargo and ferry ports, airports and Channel Tunnel.

The **North East and South West are much more remote** and are considered by many businesses as being too far away from the economic core.

Transport links to Manchester and Birmingham are very good, including the M1/M6 and West Coast Mainline. Other more distant areas still suffer as a result of their remote geographical location and remain in the economic periphery.

Infrastructure

Infrastructure refers to the built environment of services, such as transport, that allow the rest of the economy to flourish. Infrastructure projects often cost a lot of money but can bring big benefits.

London and the South East have benefited greatly from the **Channel Tunnel** as well as airport expansion at **Heathrow and Stansted**. Manchester Airport's second runway allowed the

▲ Fig.122 **CrossRail tunnel**

airport to expand to become Britain's third busiest. Sometimes infrastructure projects can be controversial because of the huge sums involved and the potential for environmental damage.

The **CrossRail** project should open in 2018. This is a £15 billion scheme to tunnel train lines from Reading to Kent, under London. People complain that too much is spent in the South East further deepening the 'North-South divide.'

HS2, the high speed train link, to Birmingham from London, has an estimated cost of around £17.5 billion. It will not be finished until 2026. Further high speed lines to connect Manchester and Leeds will not be finished until 2033 at the earliest. Some fear that rising costs will lead to the cancellation of these new lines.

▼ Fig.121 **The Channel Tunnel carried 19 million lorries in 2015**

Changing economies

No economy stays the same. As factories expand, their workers earn more money. New jobs are created in the services that support the factory and its workforce. Money spent by those workers results in a **further expansion of service jobs**.

However, countries are part of an international world of both trading and competition. If an industry cannot compete on price or quality with goods or services produced elsewhere then that industry will decline or perhaps close altogether.

From 1800 to 1870 Britain produced more than half of the world's iron. It lead the world in steel production. In 1914 Britain produced 8 million tonnes of steel but Germany, with its newer

more efficient furnaces produced 14 million tonnes. Both were overtaken by USA, which by 1920 was making 60 million tonnes each year.

Today China produces the world's cheapest steel. Chinese steel works produced 71 million tonnes in March 2016 alone. In these situations, either an industry modernises, is protected by its government or it is at risk of closing down altogether.

The 20th Century saw a steady decline in British heavy industry. Many industries were **rescued by nationalisation** after the Second World War.

Since the 1980s many of these heavy industries have continued their long-term decline or closed altogether.

▲ Fig.123 **The Teesside steelworks, at Redcar in the North East, closed in 2015 with the loss of 1,700 jobs in the local area.**

There are different **c**auses and consequences of development within the UK which has geographical patterns.

Can government policy effect economic development?

Over the last 25 years Britain has become more and more **dependent on its service sector**. It provides jobs for the population and pays the taxes that fund public services. This is especially true of the **finance and banking sector**, much based in the City of London. In 2014 banking was responsible for **£31 billion of taxes** received by the government.

Government policy has been to encourage foreign banks to set up headquarters in London. This was partly the reason for the re-development of the London Docklands in the 1980s: to create a new home for financial corporations.

Government policy is always controversial. Some say that it doesn't matter what sector the jobs are in, as long as there are jobs. Others say that Britain's **declining manufacturing base** leaves the economy **at risk from problems in the financial markets**, as occurred in 2007/8.

Past governments have protected some industries. Struggling industries

Fig.124 **Oakdale, the last deep coal mine in the Gwent valleys**

were nationalised (bought by the government) to keep them employing people. In the last 40 years this policy was reversed and some industries allowed to close.

Coal mining used to be a mass industry, employing 1.2 million miners in 1920. Over the years government policy towards mining changed. In the 1980s and 1990s most deep coal mines were closed. Today, just 4,000 workers are employed in coal mining, mostly in open-cast mines in Scotland.

Government action can help develop new industries. Subsidies for

wind and solar energy in the early 21st Century helped these industries develop. A reduction in those same subsidies, in the years since 2010, saw a slow down in the growth of these new industries.

Government decisions on big infrastructure projects such, as HS2 or new nuclear power plants, can help drive investment and create jobs.

In contrast, a government decision not to back an industry can lead to job losses and economic decline for the areas where these industries operate.

Thinking it through

1. Using examples, distinguish between the **economic core and economic periphery** of the UK. (4)

2. Define what is meant by the letters **GVA**. (1)

3. Distinguish between **GVA and GDP**. (2)

4. In terms of GVA, where is the **most productive region** of the UK? (1)

5. Why might Aberdeen and North East Scotland be considered as an economic **resource frontier**? (2)

6. What is meant by the term **de-industrialisation**? (1)

7. Suggest why the **Inner London regions** are so important to the UK economy. (3)

8. Suggest reasons why **London receives more investment than Cornwall.** (3)

9. Suggest reasons why large **infrastructure projects may help a region** in both the **short and long term**. (4)

10. Explain why the decline of industries such as coal mining, ship building or steel manufacture can have a **damaging effect on local economies.** (4)

11. Using examples, explain how **government policies can impact on the economic development** of different regions within the UK. (6)

12. Using the example of Salford Quays, explain why local and national government may wish to **redevelop areas** where previous industries have declined or closed. (4)

Your Revision checklist

You need to be confident about describing, and offering explanations for, **Britain's role in the world** and its connections with other countries. This should include an overview of the **UK's current major trading partners** and include our **principal exports and imports** (pp.31-33). You should also be clear about the different aspects of the **UK's geographical diversity**. This should cover patterns of **employment, average income, life expectancy, educational attainment, ethnicity and access to broadband** (pp.34-37).

You need to recognise the **causes of uneven development within the UK**. This understanding should include important factors such as **geographical location, economic change, infrastructure and government policies** (pp.38-40). You should learn **examples from around the UK** to show your depth of understanding of these issues.

You must also learn about **one case study** covering the consequences of **economic growth and/or decline for one place or region in the UK**. The case study in this book is **Salford Quays** (p.41-43) which has seen both **economic growth, decline and subsequent regeneration** over the last 120 years.

There are different causes and consequences of development within the UK which has geographical patterns.

The rise and fall, and rise again, of Salford Quays

Salford Quays, formerly known as the Manchester Docks, is an area that has undergone industrial expansion, decline and regeneration over the last 120 years. It is typical of many parts of Britain with an industrial heritage that have had to adjust to a process called de-industrailsation.

The Manchester Docks, located at the end of the **Manchester Ship Canal**, was once Britain's third-busiest port, despite being 40 miles inland. Today, renamed Salford Quays, the area is a

thriving centre for the creative industries with **MediaCityUK**, home to several production arms of the BBC, Granada Studios and the Lowry Theatre.

The **Manchester Docks closed in 1983 with the loss of 3,000 job**s. The docks fell into disrepair. Surrounding areas of working class housing became blighted with unemployment and urban decline. **Salford City Council** acquired 90 hectares of the former docks and rebranded them as **Salford Quays**.

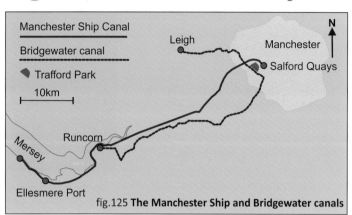

fig.125 **The Manchester Ship and Bridgewater canals**

The Manchester Ship Canal

The **Manchester Ship Canal stretches 36 miles** from the south bank of the River Mersey at Eastham Locks to its terminus in Salford Quays, formerly the Manchester Docks.

As Manchester expanded rapidly during the industrial revolution it found itself stifled by excessive port fees in Liverpool. At times it was cheaper to import goods via Hull on the east coast. Demands grew for a new canal to link the Mersey estuary with Manchester.

This plan was opposed by the businessmen of Liverpool. **Initial plans for a canal were rejected by Parliament.** The public outcry from the people of Manchester, which included a petition with 200,000 names, forced a re-think and **construction started on the canal in 1887.**

As with many large projects, then and now, it was soon **behind schedule and way over budget** and needed an injection of cash from the Manchester Corporation (council). An average of **12,000 people worked to dig the canal**, rising to 17,000 at peak times. A total of 41 million cubic metres of soil and rock were excavated.

In 1894 the canal was opened by Queen Victoria. The entire project had cost £15 million (equivalent to around

£1.65 billion today.)

Two years after the ship canal opened, a local businessman began the construction of **Trafford Park.** Just south of the Manchester Docks, Trafford Park was to be the world's **first planned industrial estate** and still remains Europe's largest.

However, as ships began to get larger in the post WW2 era, the **width of the locks along the ship canal restricted access to the new larger vessels.** Freight volumes rapidly declined, signalling the beginning of the end for the Manchester Docks.

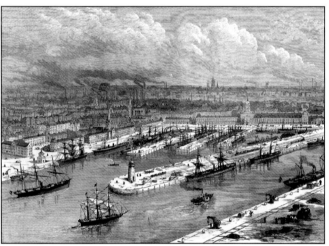

fig.126 "THE PROPOSED MANCHESTER SHIP CANAL: INTENDED DOCKS AT MANCHESTER", published in *The Illustrated London News* February 1883.

First steps to regeneration

The first step in the Quays regeneration was to **improve the water quality**, which were heavily polluted. Dams were built to separate the docks from the ship canal. The waters were aerated with compressed air to improve the water quality. After two years **12,000 fish were released into the waters** of the docks.

With improving water quality, the land areas could be improved. **New housing, bridges and roads were built**, as well as a waterside promenade. Small busi-

nesses were encouraged to relocate onto the Quays.

For any urban regeneration to be successful the area needs to feel **vibrant** if it is to draw people back. In the early days, many of the new residents complained that the Quays felt lifeless after dark. What the area needed was not just houses and jobs but things to do in the evening. **The Lowry Theatre**, retail outlet and cinema was intended to fill this need, bringing evening life to the Quays.

▲ fig.127 **Sailing the ship canal**

Today the Ship Canal is owned by Peel Holdings. The canal is increasing its freight movements once more: this time into the new Port Salford, down channel of Salford Quays. Peel Holdings estimate the Ship Canal will be carrying **100,000 containers each year by 2030.**

There are different causes and consequences of development within the UK which has geographical patterns.

Quays on the up

By the early 1990s the regeneration of the Quays had cost in the region of £280 million. But the spending didn't stop there.

Iconic buildings

The regeneration plan had included the idea of a **regional arts centre.** This dream became a reality with the completion of the Lowry, which opened in 2000. Its construction was part-funded by the National Lottery. The Lowry contains a 1800-seat theatre and an art gallery housing some of the paintings of L.S. Lowry, after whom the building takes its name.

Across an open plaza from the theatre is the **Lowry Outlet** shopping centre, above which climbs the **Imperial Point** residential, building.

▲ Fig.129 **Walking to Work, L.S.Lowry**

Fig.128 **Salford Quays at night**

Across from the Lowry on the south bank of the Ship Canal is the **Imperial War Museum North**. The building was designed by world-famous architect **Daniel Libeskind.** Its design, with its sloping ceiling and walls and disconcerting 'air shard' tower was to stand as a metaphor for a world shattered by war. The museum has received over **3 million visitors** since it opened in 2002.

Transport links improved

In 1999, a new line was opened on the **Metrolink**, Greater Manchester's light rapid transit system. The new tram line connected Salford Quays with Manchester and Eccles. With great foresight, the Metrolink stops were constructed well before the BBC was persuaded to move some of its departments into the new

MediaCityUK development.

Despite the frequent tram times, many people still travel to work in the Quays by car. **Car parking is a problem**, with many cars parked along grass verges in Trafford Park to the south.

In 2007, the BBC moved five departments including **Children's TV** and **Radio 5 Live** out of London. They sold their Manchester city centre headquarters. The BBC moved into a purpose-built complex called **MediaCityUK** at the Quays.

Granada TV also closed their Manchester city centre studios and moved their production to the Quays. **Coronation Street** is now filmed in studios across the Ship Canal from MediaCityUK, next door to the Imperial War Museum.

Housing - low rise to high rise

The first new housing built in Salford Quays in the late 1980s were 'low-rise' terraces and mews housing on **Merchant Quay** overlooking Dock 7. These were followed by town houses and apartments. No building was greater than the four storey apartments which were built in the mid-1990s on **Grain Wharf,** adjacent to Dock 9.

Later properties have built upwards. The success of the redevelopment pushed land prices higher and suggested a bigger return for

developers. **Imperial Point** rises 16 storeys above the Millennium Bridge. The three towers of the **NV Building**s rise 18 storeys (55 metres) above the waterside of Dock 9.

Not all constructions have been immediately successful. The property slump after the financial crisis of 2008 forced **City Lofts** to put their unsold flats into receivership. However, with the opening of the MediaCityUK development, the demand for property was once again on the rise. Two new developments, **The Heart** and **Number One**, rise 22 storeys above the Quays.

KEY TERMS

De-industrialisation: the process by which the employment structure of an economy changes from one in which production and manufacturing are the core employers to one in which services are more significant. This can often leave former industrial areas suffering high levels of unemployment and poverty.

Regeneration: The process, often encouraged or led by government bodies whereby areas blighted by unemployment and other problems are improved. This process often involves working with the private sector to generate new job opportunities.

Fig.130 **NV Buildings over Huron Basin, Salford Quays**

There are different causes and consequences of development within the UK which has geographical patterns.

Manchester: city life at the heart of the North West

A brief history of an industrial city

Manchester has been described a **'the beating heart of the north west of England.'** It is both a city, and a metropolitan borough, within the county of Greater Manchester. Governed by **Manchester City Council**, the city has a growing population of over 520,000 (2015). The conurbation of **Greater Manchester contains over 2.5 million people.**

Manchester's history began with a settlement around the **Roman Fort of Mancunium,** established around 79 AD near the confluence of the Irwell and Medlock rivers. The fort was eventually abandoned by the Romans. Manchester remained a **small and insignificant township** throughout medieval times, albeit one with a flourishing linen and woollen textile industry. This industry

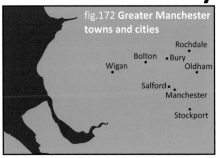

fig.172 **Greater Manchester towns and cities**

was started by Flemish weavers who settled in the area in the 14th Century.

The opening of the **Bridgewater Canal in 1761** allowed coal to be brought into the town at much cheaper rates than previously. This coal, combined with the advent of steam power and the flat land available for building mills, saw Manchester's industry expand dramatically and its population grew rapidly.

Canals, cotton and coal were the secrets to Manchester growth during the industrial revolution. Nicknamed **"Cottonopolis"** during Victorian times, Manchester gained city status in 1853, the first new British city for 300 years.

Manchester exported cotton goods across the world. In Australia and New Zealand, "Manchester" is still used as the collective term for cotton sheets, pillow cases and towels.

The cotton trade accelerated after the opening of the **Manchester Ship Canal** in 1894. The canal allowed ships direct access to the Manchester docks, cutting transport costs and boosting profits.

The cotton mills attracted people from Scotland, Wales and across England for work. New inventions, and an expansion of transport links, further spurred Manchester's growth. **The city became the world's premier industrial city and a show case for British capitalism.**

While **cotton declined in importance** in the 20th Century, Manchester remained an important industrial city, with nearby **Trafford Park** hosting numerous large factories. This made the city a target for **significant aerial bombing raids** during the Second World War.

▲ Fig.173 **Manchester 1900**

Greater Manchester

Today, Manchester is one of the ten **metropolitan borough councils** that make up **Greater Manchester**. Covering 1,276 km^2 and with a population of 2.8 million, Greater Manchester is the **second largest conurbation** in the UK.

Fig.174 **Greater Manchester**

Radical Manchester

The conditions for the workers in the mills and in their homes were often appalling. This was the subject of Friedrich Engels' famous book *The Condition of the Working Class in England in 1844*.

Fig.175 **Friedrich Engels**

Engels, alongside Karl Marx whom he met in a Manchester library, went on to write the *Communist Manifesto* in 1848.

Manchester became one of the centres of the Chartist movement campaigning for the right to vote for working people. It witnessed the birth of the British trade union movement, with the first TUC congress held in the city in 1868. It later become an important city in the development of the Labour Party, as well as the suffragette movement campaigning for votes for women.

Post-war Manchester

In the post-war eras, Manchester set out to clear slums and repair bomb-damaged homes, building thousands of **council houses**. While some estates were sought-after and cherished places to live. Other estates, like the 1960s-built Hulme Crescents, were badly designed, poorly maintained and soon became run-down.

As ships grew larger, the Ship Canal was unable to carry the new breed of modern container ships which now docked in Liverpool. **Manchester's docks finally closed in 1982, with the loss of 3000 jobs.** This was matched with industrial decline. Manufacturing jobs were lost to competition from developing industries abroad. **150,000 manufacturing jobs were lost between 1960 and 1983.** Manchester's future, at times, looked bleak.

In more recent years **Manchester has undergone an urban revival** with the city once again able to claim a central place in the economy and culture of the UK.

Cities have distinct challenges and ways of life, influenced by its people, culture and geography.

What are the patterns of migration to Manchester?

The history of Manchester over the last two centuries is like most other cities; a history of migration. Initially the city grew as it drew in agricultural workers looking for jobs in the expanding mills.

These workers were joined by **thousands of Irish labourers**, many of whom built the canals and railways.

In the 20th Century international migration continued to shape the city. **Jews, fleeing persecution in the Russian empire**, settled in Cheetham Hill where there are still several well attended synagogues. Today, the Jewish population in Manchester numbers around 25,000. In 2014 a 13 mile long 'eruv' was established. This is a symbolic boundary that allows orthodox religious Jews to carry or push certain items outside of their homes on the Sabbath.

Migration in the 1950s and 1960s saw large numbers of **West Indians** settle in wards such as Moss Side, while **Pakistani immigrants** moved to Longsight, Rusholme and Cheetham

▼ fig.176 **Moss Side's Carnival celebrates diversity**

Hill. Rusholme's famous Curry Mile has been expanding since the late 1960s, providing Pakistani, Indian and, more recently, Arabic and Afghan cuisine. It is said to be the largest concentration of South Asian restaurants outside the Indian sub continent.

In the 1990s refugees from **Yugoslavia, Iraq** and **Somalia** have made their homes in the city. In some parts of Manchester there are thirty or more native languages spoken by children at school. In more recent times, migration has seen people moving from **Eastern Europe**. The Polish Catholic churches

established by refugees after the Second World War experienced a revival in congregations after 2005.

Manchester had a small **Chinese** population at the start of the 20th Century. Manchester's China Town, which is now the third largest in Europe, began to expand in the 1950s as workers moved from Hong Kong. The first restaurant, Ping Hong opened in 1948. The famous Faulkner Street arch was made in China and erected in Manchester in 1987.

▼ fig.178 **Ethnicity in Manchester**

All Ages	503,127
All White groups	66.6%
Mixed	4.6%
Indian	2.3%
Pakistani	8.5%
Bangladeshi	1.3%
Other Asian	2.3%
Black Caribbean	1.9%
Black African	5.1%
Other Black	1.6%
Chinese	2.7%
Other	3.1%
All Non-White groups	33.4%

source: 2011, Census

Manchester's ethnic diversity

fig.177 **Ethnic groups in Manchester by ward, 2011**

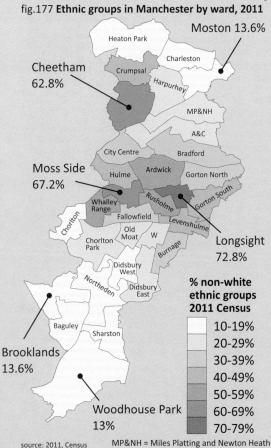

Moston 13.6%
Heaton Park
Charleston
Cheetham 62.8%
Crumpsal
Harpurhey
MP&NH
A&C
City Centre
Bradford
Moss Side 67.2%
Hulme
Ardwick
Gorton North
Whalley Range
Rusholme
Gorton South
Fallowfield
Levenshulme
Chorlton
Old Moat
W
Longsight 72.8%
Chorlton Park
Burnage
Didsbury West
Northeden
Didsbury East
Baguley
Sharston
Brooklands 13.6%
Woodhouse Park 13%

% non-white ethnic groups 2011 Census
10-19%
20-29%
30-39%
40-49%
50-59%
60-69%
70-79%

source: 2011, Census
MP&NH = Miles Platting and Newton Heath
A&C = Ancoats and Clayton
W = Withington

Migrants often end up **settling where there is available housing and many pre-exisiting social networks** to support new arrivals. This is true of students moving to a new town to start a university course or a family moving from India or Poland.

As **inner city areas often have cheaper houses**, many migrants find themselves settling in these places on arrival. Community groups spring up, often based on places of worship. These provide social support for new arrivals.

Over time some migrants may move to more expensive housing or gain access to social housing after serving time on housing waiting lists. This then **opens up the area for new migrants to settle.**

This pattern of migration creates **concentrations of people from a certain national or ethnic background in one particular place.** These areas can become associated with one ethnic group.

17% of the population of Moss Side is Black African and 10% Black Caribbean. Nearly 36% of the population of Longsight are of Pakistani origin. **Longsight is the only ward in Manchester where white British residents are not the largest single ethnic group.**

KEY TERMS

Asylum seeker: someone who claims to be a refugee but has yet to be accepted as a refugee by the country to which they have fled.

Economic migrant: someone who moves from one place to another to find work. Economic migrants usually move because they can get better pay in their new 'host' country than they can by staying in the 'donor' country from which the come.

Refugee: a person fleeing persecution on the basis of race, gender, religion, political beliefs and other factors that give them a 'well-founded fear' for their life and safety.

Cities have distinct challenges and ways of life, influenced by its people, culture and geography.

How are the areas in Manchester different?

Manchester has 32 electoral wards, each of which elects 3 of the 96 councillors who sit on Manchester City Council. Looking at data for each of these wards can help geographers look for repeated, or exceptional, patterns.

These patterns are used to help predict future changes in the city, or help inform decisions about spending by both national and local government.

Manchester is ranked as the 5th 'most deprived' area in the United Kingdom. This ranking is determined by bringing together a range of data about income, employment, education, crime and the environment to create multiple **'indices of deprivation.'**

By converting the data onto a choropleth (density shading) map it is becomes obvious that while Manchester overall is rated poorly for deprivation, this is not true of all areas in Manchester.

Fig.179 shows the percentage of children living in low income households. Some of the areas have very high figures such as Ancoats and Clayton, where 49.7%

of children live in very poor households. There are similar figures for Moss Side, Harpurhey and Miles Platting. Meanwhile in Chorlton, just 1 in 13 children lives in poverty.

As with all statistics, they cannot tell the complete picture. **The City Centre ward has just 8.5% of children in income deprivation.** Its total population in 2015 was 20,976. Closer analysis shows that in 2015 there were only 523 children under the age of 15 in City Centre ward. In Moss Side there were 5002 under 15s out of a population of 21,088. So in 2015 there were about 45 children in the City Centre living in poverty compared to 2430 children in Moss Side living in poor households.

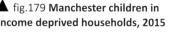

% children living in income deprivation
- 0-9.9%
- 10-19.9%
- 20-29.9%
- 30-39.9%
- 40-49.9%

▲ fig.179 **Manchester children in income deprived households, 2015**

Income deprivation

One of the most significant indices of deprivation is that of **income deprivation** or people living in poor households. For children, Manchester is ranked 5th nationwide, having **34.3% of all children living in income deprived families.**

For families as a whole the city does better, being ranked 7th with **24.2% of all families in receipt of state benefits** because they are out of work or their pay is low.

However, for people over the age of 60, Manchester does very poorly. It is ranked 4th for deprivation in this category. **36.3 % or 1 in 3 people over 60 live in poor households.**

Crime deprivation

Crime deprivation score
- <0
- 0.0-4.9
- 5.0-7.4
- 7.5-9.9
- 10.0-12.4
- >12.5

▲ fig.180 **Crime deprivation indices by Manchester ward, 2015**

Manchester is ranked 14th nationwide for crime deprivation **but individual wards still show marked differences.** These figures collate incidents of crimes of violence, burglary, theft and criminal damage. While Harpurhey, in north Manchester, receives one of the worst scores in the country (mostly caused by burglary and criminal damage), Woodhouse Park in the south receives one of the best.

The City Centre does not score well. It has lots of businesses which experience crimes such as **shoplifting**. There is also a significant problem with **alcohol-fuelled violence**, especially at the weekends.

Heaton Park received a lower than expected score because of the high number of thefts which occurred during the weekend Parklife Festival.

Meanwhile the two Didsbury wards achieve high scores, alongside Ardwick near the city centre. **Areas with good community coherence do better than those areas with a more transient population.**

Living environment

Living environment score
- 10-19
- 20-29
- 30-39
- 40-49
- >50

▲fig.181 **Living environment indices of deprivation by Manchester ward.**

The indices for the **living environment** combine statistics about the quality of housing (indoor sub-domain) with figures for air pollution and traffic accidents (outdoor domain). Here **Manchester does better** than elsewhere and is ranked 35th.

The big change is that the City Centre has the lowest score of all the wards - achieving a score of 71, way behind Hulme on 43. Woodhouse Park, which contains Manchester Airport, achieves a score of 19. Parts of Manchester that do badly overall, such as Harpurhey, do better on this environment score because of the **high quality and good maintenance of much of the social housing.**

The **City Centre achieves a low score because of very high traffic congestion**, which increases air pollution and the number of traffic accidents. There are also a number of older flats without central heating in the City Centre ward. This reduces the area's score for the indoor living sub-domain.

59

Cities have distinct challenges and ways of life, influenced by its people, culture and geography.

What is the quality of life like in Manchester?

Manchester has a problem with many residents, and especially the elderly and children, living in income-deprived households.

In January 2013, the retiring Bishop of Manchester, Nigel McCulloch, spoke out saying, "Over the past 10 years I have seen **increasing vibrancy and investment in Greater Manchester, which make some parts look relatively prosperous. But at the same time the gap between rich and poor has been widening**, under governments of any political persuasions."

Life remains tough for many people in Manchester, struggling with numerous social and economic problems.

However, despite its obvious problems of poverty and social deprivation, the city continues to expand. The growth of the creative industries, associated with the

▲ fig.182 **China Town arch, Faulkner Street.**

opening of **MediaCityUK** on Salford Quays, has brought many more well-paid workers to the city. For those with more money to spend there are **many positive attractions to living in the Manchester.**

There is a well-developed **social and entertainment scene** - from cinemas to pubs, clubs and bars. These have expanded

in many areas, such as Chorlton and Didsbury, and are not just confined to the city centre.

Manchester has a **vibrant shopping centre** around Market Street and Piccadilly. The many restaurants of **China Town**, and bars of the **Northern Quarter**, cater for a wide variety of tastes. Manchester's famous **'Gay Village'** centred on Canal Street, draws in thousands at the weekends and tens of thousands during the annual **'Pride' Mardi Gras festival** every August.

The city's two Premier League football clubs, **Manchester City and Manchester United**, each bring millions of pounds into the city, with money spent by supporters on hotels, food and public transport.

The football stadiums, along the Old Trafford ground of Lancashire Cricket Club, also host popular **summer music concerts by international artists.**

Learning in the city

Manchester has one of the largest full-time student populations outside of London. There are around **85,000 students** who attend Manchester University, UMIST, Manchester Metropolitan University (MMU), the Royal Northern College of Music (RNCM) and Salford University. This creates great opportunities for Manchester but also results in a number of issues.

With so many highly-trained students graduating each year, **Manchester does not have as many skills shortages as other cities.** While many graduates move away in search of work, many others have enjoyed their years in Manchester so much that they chose to stay. **Manchester has a higher proportion of residents with university degrees than the national average.**

The high proportion of younger people means that Manchester has a **vibrant youth culture**: with many music venues, nightclubs, bars and other places of entertainment. These create jobs, although many are often filled by students working part-time.

However, there are a number of issues.

⊙ With so many students looking for accommodation many house are bought up by landlords to rent. This pushes up general house prices and makes it harder

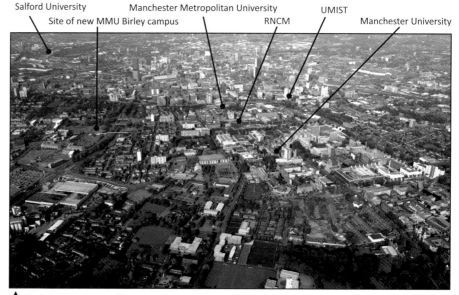

Salford University
Site of new MMU Birley campus
Manchester Metropolitan University
RNCM
UMIST
Manchester University

▲ fig.183 **Manchester from the air. Manchester University campus shown with red dottted line**

for local families to buy.

⊙ Many of these properties can be poorly maintained by the landlords. Shared student accommodation can also be **a target for burglaries**. They tend to have higher concentrations of electronic goods such as televisions and computers than family houses.

⊙ Local businesses become dominated by the **student market with bars, cafes and takeaways** becoming more common to the detriment of other shops. This process has been called **'studentisation'.**

⊙ The City Council may receive less local taxation because households with 100% student occupants are exempt from paying council tax.

⊙ Areas around the universities may become **over-crowded with parked cars**. This has resulted in the council imposing parking restrictions in areas close to the universities. On **'Gridlock Sunday'** large areas of south Manchester become jammed with traffic, as parents drop off their children at the start of a new term.

What are the future challenges for Manchester?

Manchester successfully met the challenges of the 19th Century building the canals and railways and providing clean water for its residents. **Today, many Mancunians believe that their city can again successfully meet the challenges of the 21st Century.**

However, just as in the 1900s where not everyone agreed about the way forward, the **future direction of the city is hotly contested.**

Most would agree that the city faces social, economic and environmental challenges. These must be faced if Manchester is to continue to be a successful and popular place to live.

SOCIAL COHESION

One of the social issues facing Manchester is one of successfully **integrating its large immigrant community, without creating tensions with existing groups.** While many 'white British' Mancunians welcome the multi-cultural nature of the city, others feel threatened, and fear the loss of what they believe is a 'British' way of life.

Racist attacks on immigrants and minority ethnic groups, while not common, do occur with some frequency. The number of reported racially-aggravated crimes rose in the aftermath of the 2016 'Brexit' vote. Eastern European migrants reported being abused in the street and told to 'go home.' There have also been desecrations of Jewish cemeteries and Islamophobic attacks on members of Manchester's Muslim community.

Members of Manchester Afro-Caribbean and African communities report discrimination when it comes to gaining good jobs or even getting an interview.

Many argue that racism and xenophobia flourish when people feel 'under siege'. They argue that the best way to tackle racism is not just to confront racist ideas but to 'drain the swamp' of poverty in which desperate people blame other poor people for their problems.

ECONOMIC PROSPERITY

Manchester has a long-term problem with income deprivation, with **thousands of families living on low wages.** In past decades, Manchester City Council was a major employer, but budget cuts since the financial crisis of 2008 has seen the City Council shed thousands of jobs.

▲ fig.184 **The clean and redeveloped streets of Ancoats, Manchester. Some say they feel sterile. Others say it is a great improvement on the decay that went before.**

While many jobs in Manchester are well-paid, many more are not. This leaves many working families still having to claim benefits to make ends meet. In 2015, one in four jobs in Greater Manchester paid below the 'living wage' of £7.85 per hour.

In 2014, the government announced plans to develop a 'Northern Powerhouse' centred on the cities of Manchester, Liverpool, Leeds and Newcastle. This initiative was intended to bring in extra investment to the region. Part of this plan involves the election of a **Greater Manchester Mayor** to be elected in 2017. Some claim that this is just a gimmick dreamt up by the London government. Others express hope that any **new investment will help reduce some of the region's social and economic problems.**

ENVIRONMENTAL SUSTAINABILITY

As we saw on page 59, the centre of Manchester suffers from 'living environment deprivation' due to traffic congestion and associated pollution.

Congestion is one of the most significant problems facing all major cities. Car ownership seems to grow even faster than the urban population.

In 2008, Greater Manchester residents rejected a plan for congestion charging, similar to London, which was proposed by the local councils. The scheme would have seen vehicles charged to enter the M60

zone and a further charge levied to enter the centre of Manchester. In return residents were promised improved public transport. **However, 78.9% voted against the plan and it was scrapped.**

▲ fig.185 **Building work for the Metrolink in St. Peter's Square. Getting ready for the second city crossing.**

Another environmental issue is waste disposal. Cities produce a vast quantity of waste every day and Manchester is no different. **Greater Manchester produces over 3,000 tonnes of rubbish a day.**

Waste water is also a significant issue. At peak times the Davyhulme Waste Water Treatment Plant must deal with **30,000 litres of waste water every second.** Much of this contains sewage, detergents and other pollutants. The water must be cleaned and treated before being discharged to join the water flowing in the Manchester Ship Canal.

61

Cities have distinct challenges and ways of life, influenced by its people, culture and geography.

How is Manchester becoming a sustainable city?

▲ fig.186 **Metrolink is a great transport success.**

Metrolink: reducing congestion

The very successful **Metrolink tram system** in Greater Manchester has continued to expand from its modest beginning in 1992. The first line opened between Bury and Altrincham. Since then six more lines have been added to the system connecting Manchester with Eccles and Salford Quays, Oldham and Rochdale, Ashton-under-Lyne, Chorlton and Disdbury and Wythenshawe and Manchester Airport.

In 2015, the electric trams carried 34.3 million passengers over the 92km of track.

A second city crossing through Manchester opened in early 2017. A new line through Trafford Park to the Trafford Centre is scheduled to open in 2020.

▲ fig.187 **Recycling & incineration have cut landfill.**

Cutting down on the waste

The **Greater Manchester Waste Disposal Authority** works with Greater Manchester councils to dispose of the rubbish produced in the city. The Authority processes 1.1 million tonnes of waste each year. In recent years rates of recycling have risen sharply. Different wheelie bins are used to collect different types of rubbish for recycling or disposal.

The **GMWDA has 43 facilities over 23 sites** processing, recycling, composting and incinerating waste. The authority recycled **50% of waste in 2016**. Around 56 MW of electricity, enough for 12,000 homes, was generated from Greater Manchester's waste using anaerobic digestion, incineration and methane collected from the City's landfill sites.

▲ fig.188 **Beehives on the City Art Gallery roof.**

Greening the city

Green space and trees are important in any city. **Trees reduce air pollution** and create a more attractive urban environment for residents. The **City of Trees** project aims to plant millions of trees, along streets and in orchards and woods, as well as better manage the many hectares of existing woodland already within Greater Manchester. **By 2017 volunteers had planted 55,000 trees.**

Meanwhile, **beekeepers have been bringing their hives into the city**, helping to bring a more natural balance to the city's ecosystems. There are bee hives on the roofs of many of the city's buildings including the Printworks entertainment complex, City Art Gallery and Manchester Cathedral.

Thinking it through

1. Manchester has an **unusual population structure**, as shown in fig.189 opposite.

a) What percentage of the population is **aged between 20 and 30 years**? (1)

b) What percentage of the population is **aged under 5**? (1)

c) **Suggest reasons** for the population structure shown in fig.189. (4)

2. Describe how immigration has impacted on the **cultural development** of Manchester. (4)

3. Describe the distribution of different groups from **Manchester's ethnic minorities** as shown by the 2011 census and fig.177 on p.58. (4)

4. Outline some of the **social and economic problems** facing Manchester. (6)

5. Describe ways in which the City of Manchester has

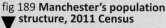

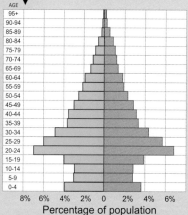

fig 189 **Manchester's population structure, 2011 Census** ▼

Percentage of population

attempted to **become more sustainable.** (6)

6. Outline the **positive and negative impacts of having a high student population** in Manchester. (4)

7. Describe some of the **issues associated with deprivation** which affect cities such as Manchester. (6)

62

Cities have distinct challenges and ways of life, influenced by its people, culture and geography.

How do different air masses affect Britain's climate?

Air masses are large bodies of air that have distinctive characteristics such as temperature, humidity and cloud type. They are formed over a source region and bring with them the characteristics of that region.

For example, an air mass forming over a warm sea will bring warm, moist air and rain. An air mass forming over a cold area of land will bring dry, cool air and clear skies.

Air masses are named after their source region. If they are formed over the sea they are referred to as **maritime**. If they form over land, then they are **continental**. The other factor is the latitude of the source region. Those forming to the south of Britain are referred to as **Tropical** air masses, while those forming to the north are either **Polar** or **Arctic**.

Figure 191 shows the main air masses that influence the weather of the British Isles. Each has very different characteristics making Britain's weather extremely unpredictable.

When two air masses, with different sets of characteristics, meet they do not mix. As a result the warmer, less dense air rises over the cooler and denser air. This meeting zone is called a front.

The rising air cools as it expands with altitude and water vapour begins to condense into cloud droplets. These tiny droplets then join together by collisions until they are large enough to fall from the sky as rain. This creates what is referred to as **frontal rain.** As Britain is at a meeting point for several air masses, we recieve a lot of frontal rain, as well as the relief rainfall common over the hills and mountains.

Fig.190 **Approaching weather front**

Britains air masses

Tropical continental (Tc): This air mass forms over North Africa and the Sahara Desert It is most common during the summer months of June, July and August. Our highest temperatures usually occur under the influence of **Tropical continental** air and can produce 'heat waves.' Sometimes dust from the Sahara is washed out of the air during rainfall, leaving cars covered in a fine orange dust.

Tropical maritime (Tm): The source region for this air mass is over the warm waters of the Atlantic Ocean. **Tropical maritime** air is warm and moist. When a Tropical maritime air mass reaches the British Isles it brings low cloud and drizzle. The moisture may rain out over the western hills, leaving the eastern side of the country with finer weather, especially in summer.

Polar continental (Pc): This air has its source over Eastern Europe and Russia. It tends to be a winter visitor. In the summer months the land heats up so the air mass becomes classified as Tropical continental. **Polar continental** air picks up water as it passes over the North Sea. It may bring cold flurries of snow to the east coast.

Polar maritime (Pm): This air mass has its origins over Canada and Greenland. It reaches the British Isles from the north-west. **Polar maritime is the most common air mass to affect the British Isles.** This air starts off very cold and dry but picks up warmth and moisture over the Atlantic, bringing frequent showers.

Arctic maritime (Am): An **Arctic maritime** air mass has its source region over the Arctic Ocean. **Arctic maritime** air is similar to a Polar maritime air but it stays colder and drier because it passes over less sea. This air mass is not common in summer. When it does arrive it often brings cold temperatures and thunderstorms. In the winter, **Arctic maritime** air brings hail and snow to Scotland.

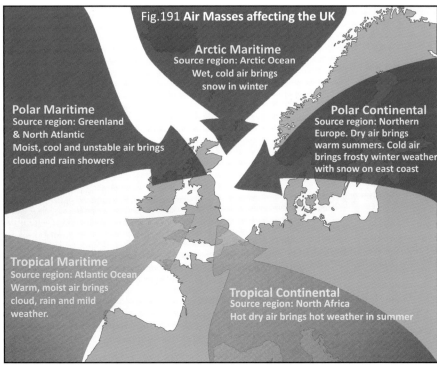

Fig.191 **Air Masses affecting the UK**

Arctic Maritime
Source region: Arctic Ocean
Wet, cold air brings snow in winter

Polar Maritime
Source region: Greenland & North Atlantic
Moist, cool and unstable air brings cloud and rain showers

Polar Continental
Source region: Northern Europe. Dry air brings warm summers. Cold air brings frosty winter weather with snow on east coast

Tropical Maritime
Source region: Atlantic Ocean
Warm, moist air brings cloud, rain and mild weather.

Tropical Continental
Source region: North Africa
Hot dry air brings hot weather in summer

The UK has a unique climate for its latitude which can create extreme weather conditions.

How do air masses and ocean currents shape our climate?

The **North Atlantic Drift** is part of the Gulf Stream, one of the most important ocean currents in the Atlantic Ocean. **This current brings warm water from the tropical seas of the Gulf of Mexico across the Atlantic Ocean towards northern Europe.** Scientists estimate that the North Atlantic Drift is responsible for making Britain's winter climate warmer by 5°C or perhaps even more. Comparing winter conditions on Norway's coast with those of northern Canada, which is on the same latitude, you can see how the North Atlantic Drift helps keep the sea ice free in winter.

The drift also impacts the weather. Warm air from the Tropics passing over a warm ocean can evaporate extra water, which is delivered later as rain.

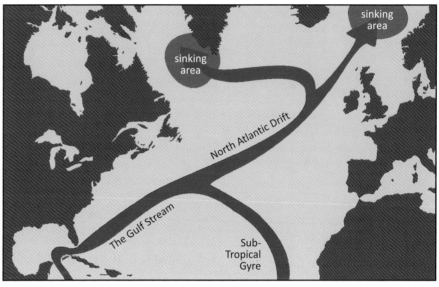

▲ fig.192 **Atlantic ocean currents, the Gulf Stream and North Atlantic Drift**

Why is Britain's weather so unpredictable?

It is often said that 'Britain has no climate, only weather.' This is because the weather changes so rapidly in these islands and is never easy to predict. Temperature may rise 5°C or more with the passage of a warm front or fall by as much as a cold front passes overhead.

This is because Britain is close to the **Polar Front** where warm Tropical air meets cold Arctic air. The front, between these air masses, produces the cloud and rain we are so familiar with.

In addition to frontal weather systems, Britain is an island and its climate is moderated by the sea. Large continental areas, such as mainland Europe, respond quickly to changes in solar radiation. They heat up quickly in the summer leading to high temperatures but cool quickly in winter. This effect is known as **continentality.**

Seas are liquids and so they warm up slowly but

▲ fig.193 **NASA satellite image of Storm Angus November, 2017**

then hold their heat longer. They act to reduce the summer temperatures of coastal areas but then keep them warmer in winter.

Moscow (55.75°N) is on the same latitude as Glasgow (55.86°N). However, Moscow is a greater distance from the ocean than Glasgow which is built at the mouth of the River Clyde.

A typical December in Glasgow will see average lows of **3°C** but lows for Moscow can plummet to an average of **-8°C**. In July Glasgow averages a **15°C** high but this high is exceeded

by Moscow's **19°C**.

Since the Atlantic Ocean is much warmer then the North Sea, the moderating effect of the water on each coast is different. In addition, the mountains of the west and north of Britain lead to more relief rainfall in these upland areas but they create a rain-shadow in the lowland east.

Britain's weather is a complex product of relief, continentality, sea and land temperatures and the interaction of different air masses.

KEY TERMS

Air mass: a large body of air with distinct characteristics taken from it place of origin.

Climate: the average weather of a place, usually measured over 30 years.

Extreme weather: these weather events occur from time to time and cause damage to property, disruption to every day activities and sometimes a loss of life.

Weather: The condition of the atmosphere at any given time, described by temperature, precipitation, wind speed and direction and visibility.

Weather front: Where two air masses meet. A warm front forms where warm air rises over cold, often bringing persistent rain. A cold front occurs where cold air undercuts warm, forcing the warm air upwards.

Weather system: a part of the atmosphere with rising air (low pressure) or falling air (high pressure) creating differing weather patterns.

The UK has a unique climate for its latitude which can create extreme weather conditions.

How do air masses cause extreme weather in the UK?

Tropical Maritime

Winter storms, 2013/14

The winter of 2013/2014 saw **Britain battered by a series of twelve storms**, each separated by a few days. This was the stormiest winter period in over 20 years. The storms swept in off the Atlantic Ocean as low pressure systems called **depressions**.

As the Atlantic Ocean is warmed by the North Atlantic Drift, these weather systems were able to pick up **lots of moisture evaporated off the warm sea surface.**

The series of storms were driven by a powerful 'jet stream', a strong upper-atmospheric wind. **Atmospheric pressures dropped to as low as 950 Mb** and wind gusted at over **100 miles per hour.** Aberdaron in Wales recorded gusts of 108mph. Meanwhile, many places received twice their average winter rainfall.

The impact of these storms was devastating to the many people affected, either by wind damage or flooding. The Environment Agency reported **over 6,000 homes flooded,** with large areas of land under water. Significant floods occurred on the **Somerset Levels and on the flood plains of the rivers Severn and Thames.**

Coastal areas were battered by strong winds and huge waves. A gas platform off the coast of Ireland recorded wave heights of 25m. In Devon, parts of the train tracks at Dawlish were washed away, cutting off South West England from train services for many months. Villages, such

Fig.194 **Storm waves batter Porthcawl, 2014**

as Porthcawl in South Wales and others along the Cornish coast, suffered severe coastal flooding and storm damage. Further inland trees were felled and powerlines brought down. **Several people were killed by flying debris.** In Scotland, heavy snowfall on the slopes of the mountains resulted in avalanches.

The government estimated the cost of **damage, caused by the 2013/14 winter storms, at £1,300 million.** Repairing the flood and wind damage to 10,465 homes was estimated at £320 million alone. However, this figure was lower than the

Fig.195 **Flood waters rise, Hebden Bridge**

Tropical Continental

A one-day heatwave, 1st July 2015

Not all heatwaves last a long-time. In July 2015 southern Britain experienced a **one-day heatwave** as hot air moved north from Spain, setting a new July record. The **highest temperatures were recorded across south-east England,** reaching the mid-30s. Temperatures were also above 30°C across parts of northern England. The heat extended to the far north of Scotland.

The hottest, record-breaking temperature was recorded at London's Heathrow Airport at 37.8°C. This was a short duration heatwave and impacts were relatively limited. However, in East Anglia the hot weather may have contributed to a **large fire which affected Thetford Forest.**

fig.197 **Heatwaves can affect ecosystems**

European Heatwave

Heatwave, summer 2003

In summer 2003, **Europe experienced a historic heatwave** that was responsible for at least **3,000 deaths in France** alone. The image shows the differences between 2001 and 2003 in day-time, land surface temperatures collected by a NASA satellite. The deep red across southern and eastern France shows where temperatures were **10°C hotter in 2003 than in 2001.**

▲ fig.196 **NASA satellite heat map**

Even in the mountains of the Alps, temperatures were very warm. **Glaciers were melting rapidly, swelling rivers and lakes to dangerously high levels.** Climbers had to be evacuated from Switzerland's Matterhorn after melting triggered the collapse of a rock face.

In London, train services were cancelled over fears that **tracks would buckle in the heat.** In Scotland the high temperatures, combined with falling water levels in rivers and streams, **threatened the spawning and survival of salmon.** In southern Europe, the hot and dry conditions sparked devastating **forest fires that killed fifteen people.**

The UK has a unique climate for its latitude which can create extreme weather conditions.

Arctic Maritime and Polar continental

Snow and freezing temperatures, December 2010

The winter of 2010 brought freezing temperatures associated with two northern sourced air masses. For two weeks, from the end of November to December 9th, Britain lay under a persistent stream of bitterly cold, **Polar continental** air from Northern Europe and Siberia. Temperatures struggled to rise above freezing during the day and **fell to below -10°C at night** and, on occasion **-20°C** in northern Scotland. **Snow fell across Scotland and Northen England.**

Milder conditions followed until cold, **Arctic maritime** air arrived on 16th December. Snow blanketed the entire country by 20th December and remained until after Boxing day. Once again daytime temperatures struggled to rise above freezing.

The impact of this weather was initially felt in Scotland, with many schools closed. **Hospital admissions increased after people injured themselves falling on the ice.**

By the start of December the disruption had spread south with Gatwick Airport closed. 400 lorries were stranded on the M25 around London. In Scotland, the Forth Road Bridge was closed for the first time since it was opened in 1964. **Hundreds of motorists were stranded overnight on the M8, M74 and A9.**

On Saturday 18th December, Heathrow Airport closed, at what is one of its busiest times of the year. The AA reported its busiest day in its 104 year history. Thousands of homes were left without electricity as powerlines came down under the weight of ice.

In the aftermath, as temperatures rose, burst pipes became a significant problem. **40,000 homes were left without mains water.**

▲ fig.198 **Britain under a blanket of snow, 2010.** *Courtesy of NASA*

Thinking it through

1. **What** is meant by the term **air mass?** (1)

2. What is the **North Atlantic Drift** and how does it affect the climate of the UK? (4)

3. Explain why the **climate of Atlantic Canada** is so **different** from that of Britain during the winter. (3)

4. What are the characteristics of a **Tropical continental** air mass? (2)

5. What are the characteristics of a **Tropical maritime** airmass? (2)

6. What happens when **two air masses** with different characteristics meet? (2)

7. What is meant by the term **extreme flooding**? (1)

8. Why can Polar maritime, Arctic maritime or Polar continental air **cause problems** in the UK? (3)

9. With reference to examples, what are the **economic impacts** of severe weather caused by different air masses. (6)

10. "**Severe weather caused by Tropical maritime air is more of a problem to the UK than that caused by Tropical continental air.**" Discuss this view with reference to examples. (8)

The cost of cold

Some estimates put the cost of the snow disruption at £1.2 billion per day, costing a total of £13 billion. This was mostly the result of a loss of business in the run-up to Christmas, as workers and shoppers stayed at home. Pre-christmas 'footfall' was down by as much as 30% in the West Midlands and 20% nationwide.

Airport disruption resulted in cancelled holidays. Insurance companies paid out £680 million in claims for burst pipe damage alone.

Livestock farmers, especially hill sheep farmers, were badly affected. Across the hills sheep were trapped in deep snowdrifts, unable to find food. Many animals froze to death.

▲ fig.199 **Hill sheep farms were badly affected, losing many sheep**

fig.200 **Heavy snow kept shoppers. at home. Shops lost sales.** ▼

Case study: Cumbria floods and Storm Desmond

On the **5th and 6th of December 2015** the British Isles were inundated with rain from **Storm Desmond.**

This storm, a **extratropical cyclone** of intense low pressure, brought with it vast quantities of water **evaporated off warm Tropical seas.** This weather phenomenon is known as an **atmospheric river** of saturated air. As this warm, moist air was forced to rise over the hills and mountains of the west of Britain and Ireland, it produced intense relief rainfall. **Storm Desmond broke the UK record for the most rain** to fall in a single 24 hour period: **341.4mm fell at the Honister Pass in the western Lake District** on the 5th/6th December. This is equivalent to 6 months of average rainfall for London!

The rain, falling on **already saturated soils,** created significant river flooding across Wales, North West England and into Scotland. Ireland and the Isle of Man were also badly affected.So much rain fell in the Pennines that **the waterfall returned at Malham Cove** in the Yorkshire Dales.

The **strong winds, which gusted in excess of 100 miles per hour,** brought down trees and powerlines, leaving thousands of homes without electricity. Lancaster University was forced to cancel lectures and evacuate students. They had found themselves with no power after an electrical substation was submerged. This **cut power to 61,000 homes.**

Travel was disrupted, with the West Coast Mainline between Preston and Carlisle closed after flooding and landslides. Trains to Scotland had to be diverted to the East Coast Mainline. Services along the North Wales line were also suspended because of flooding and debris on the tracks. **Flights out of Dublin Airport were**

▲ fig.201 **Storm Desmond was an extratropical cyclone bringing high winds and torrential rain.**

suspended because of high winds.

In the Lake District, the **A591** between Keswick and Windermere was washed away near Thirlmere. The road remained closed for until May 2016.

At the northern end of Ulswater **Pooley Bridge,** built in 1764, was **washed away by the flood waters of the River Eamont.** These waters continued downstream, joining with the swollen waters of the River Eden bringing **floods to Carlisle.**

In Keswick, where 515 properties were flooded, the Rivers **Greta** and **Derwent** recorded their highest ever flows. The water in both **Derwentwater and Bassenthwaite Lake reached record levels.**

Desmond facts

Storm type: **Extratropical cyclone.**
Formed: **3rd December 2015.**
Dissipated: **8th December 2015.**
Key dates: **5-6th December 2015.**
Lowest pressure: **939 millibars.**
Highest wind speed: **130 km/h.**
Strongest gusts: **180 km/h on Aonach Mor, Scotland.**
Heaviest rain: **341.4mm in 24 hours at Honister Pass, Lake District**
Most rain: **450mm over 72 hours at Thirlmere, Lake District**
Estimated damage **£500 million.**
Casualties: **3**

fig.202 **Heavy rain causes the waterfall at**
▼ **Malham Cove to briefly flow again.**

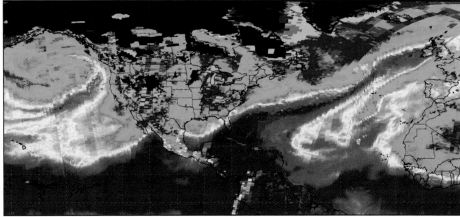

▲ fig.203 **Atmospheric River.** The 'Water Vapour Imagery' satellite photo above from the *National Weather Service Ocean Prediction Center* in the USA, show how Storm Desmond created a phenomenon known as an atmospheric river. This is a **narrow band of air with a very high moisture content**, originating over warm seas. Atmospheric rivers are responsible for around 90% of the north-south transportation of water vapour in the atmosphere. They can bring torrential rain to coastal areas. A second atmospheric river, which originated in The Philippines, can be seen in the Pacific Ocean striking the coast of North America.

67

Extreme flood hazard events are becoming more commonplace in the UK.

How did Storm Desmond affect Cumbria and Carlisle?

Storm Desmond brought severe flooding to the Cumbrian city of **Carlisle**. What shocked many people was that the floods were able to **overtop new £36 million flood defences**, built after previous flooding in 2006 and 2009.

Carlisle sits on the confluences of the **River Eden** and its tributary rivers **Petteril** and **Caldew**. These rivers, and many other tributaries, rise in the hills of the northern Pennines and Cumbrian Fells. **Their relatively small catchments mean they respond very rapidly to rainfall.** The River Eden is just 145km long. Carlisle sits on a flat floodplain and is just five kilometres upstream of the Eden's mouth in the Solway Firth.

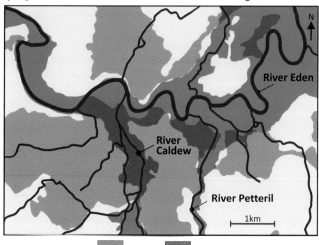
▼ fig.204 **Carlisle rivers and areas at risk of flooding**

River Eden

River Caldew

River Petteril

1km

Rivers & streams   Built up areas   Areas at risk of 1 in 100 years flooding

fig.205 **Carlisle flood waters rise** ▲

During the Desmond floods, the discharge of the River Eden **peaked at a remarkable 1,700 cumecs**. This compares to an **average discharge at Carlisle of 52 cumecs**.

This record-breaking discharge explains why some of the new flood defences failed to prevent the flooding. **They were simply overwhelmed by the volume of water.** Responding to questions about the failure of flood defences at Carlisle, Cockermouth and Keswick, Environment Agency director of flood and coastal risk, Alison Baptiste explained, **"The defences worked but the amount of rain, and the water in the river, overtopped them."**

"Whenever we build defences, we build them to a certain height but that does not mean that will prevent flooding because you can always get water levels higher than that, in which case it will go over the top. **You could build walls higher and higher but that would effectively cut the community off from the river,** meaning people would not be able to enjoy the river and the environment in which they live, which - most of the time - is flood-free."

Nonetheless, the Environment Agency **began a review of their flood planning** in light of lessons learned from the storm.

2015 Cumbria flood facts

Areas badly affected by flooding: **Carlisle, Cockermouth, Keswick, Glenridding, Pooley Bridge.**
Cost of flood damage: **Greater then £500 million.**
Homes affected: **5,200 properties flooded. 61,000 without power.**
Other damage: **3 bridges washed away, 554 damaged. A591 washed away at Thirlmere.**
Flood defences: **Carlisle's £38 million flood defences were over-topped but they saved a further 1000 properties from flooding.**

fig.206 **Carlisle under flood waters**

Thinking it through

1. Outline the climatic causes of the Cumbrian floods of **December 2015**.(4)

2. What date did Storm Desmond bring flooding to the UK? (1)

2. Which rivers flow through the **centre of Carlisle**? (2)

3. Outline the **physical reasons** why Carlisle is **particularly at risk** from river flooding. (3)

4. Outline the **social and economic reasons** why the Environment Agency doesn't build the **highest possible flood walls** along river with a flood risk. (4)

5. Describe the **economic impact of flooding** in Cumbria caused by Storm Desmond. (4)

The Cumbrian village of **Glenridding** experienced repeated flooding during the winter storm of 2015. Glenridding Beck burst its banks twice in five days during **Storm Desmond** and then again with the arrival of **Storm Eva** three weeks later. The beck carried boulders which caused considerable damage once they left the river channel with the flood waters. Find out more at **www.parishfloodgroup.org**.

fig.207 **Glenridding, Cumbria**

How does resource use impact on ecosystems?

Ecosystems link the living and non-living elements of an environment together through complex transfers of energy and nutrients. **Healthy functioning ecosystems are essential** for all life processes, including those that involve human beings.

The food that we eat is a product of complex interactions between solar energy, climate, bacteria, geology and living things, linked together through the soil. Humans often like to think of ourselves as separate from, and above, nature. However, **we are intimately linked with the ecosystems of our planet.**

All animals and plants have the capacity to alter the ecosystems within which they live. Some can radically alter the landscapes within which they find themselves. However, he changes each individual species can make are often **limited by competition with other species, predators and diseases.**

Humans, through our history of society, culture, science and technology have **effectively beaten the competition.** We have removed or reduced the number of predators through hunting. We have controlled disease and parasites through medical advances. One of the greatest challenges facing all living things is gaining enough food. Humans have met this need through agriculture.

We are now unique in the history of all species in being able to change, for better or worse, nearly every ecosystem and environment across the face of the entire planet.

▲ fig.209 **Woodland would have covered most of the British Isles** before humans cleared trees for timber and farmland.

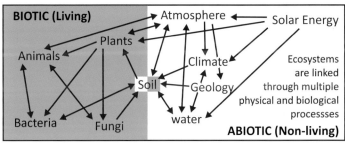
▲ fig.208 **Simplified interactions in an ecosystem**

BIOTIC (Living) — Atmosphere — Solar Energy — Plants — Animals — Climate — Soil — Geology — Bacteria — Fungi — water — ABIOTIC (Non-living)

Ecosystems are linked through multiple physical and biological processses

How is human activity altering the UK environment?

As we shall see on the next page, **Britain's landscapes, and their ecosystems, have been radically altered by farming.** There are now very few 'wild' places at all in the UK. None are true wildernesses, unaffected by human activity. This is even true of the vast moorlands of northern Scotland. Here red deer, raised for sport stalking, graze out any young saplings which try to grow.

Heather moorlands in the Pennines and North York Moors are managed for grouse shooting. To keep the heather healthy and attract grouse, the moors are burned regularly to keep the heather young and vigorous. The burning stops natural woodland cover developing by killing off any saplings that germinate.

Some environmentalists, such as George Monbiot, argue that we should **'re-wild'** some of our countryside, allowing natural succession to take place and trees to return. **'Rewilders' argue for the reintroduction of formerly native species such as beavers, lynx and even wolves.** These ecologists cite evidence from around the world about the ecological benefits of having fully functioning

ecosystems where apex predators act as a biological control on animals such as deer.

Others argue that while we may need to manage our land better, we should **leave decisions about management to the landowners and not alter faming traditions.**

▲ fig.210 **Cambrian hills: natural wilderness or sheep-grazed 'ecological desert?'**

"Two friends of mine once walked for six days across the Cambrian Mountains in mid-Wales, and did not see another human being. Yet there is scarcely any wildlife either. Cross that bleak plateau and you will see plenty of moorgrass, some tormentil and moss, a few crows, perhaps the odd pipit and skylark, but almost nothing else, except sodding sheep. The hills have been grazed to destruction."
Environmentalist, George Monbiot

KEY TERMS

Ecosystem: the living and non-living elements of an environment linked together by flows of energy and nutrients.

Landscape: the visible features of an area of land including its physical landforms and human features.

Non-renewable resource: a resource, such as fossil fuels, which cannot be replaced once they have been used.

Renewable resource: one which can be replaced or is renewed by natural processes, such as solar power.

Resources: things that are useful to human beings. They can be divided into natural (eg. soil, animals, energy) and human (skills, people, money).

Sustainability: the use of resources in such a way that they remain available for use by future generations.

How does farming affect ecosystems in the UK?

The vast majority of land (69%) in the UK is used for farming (agriculture.) Farming is the growing of crops or the raising of animals for food and other essentials of life, such as wool, textiles, leather, and fuel.

The UK was once covered in thick deciduous forests. This helped to create deep, rich and fertile soils in the thousands of years following the last glaciation. Early settlers were drawn to Britain by the excellent soils for farming.

Farming changes natural ecosystems. To grow a single species in a field as a crop competing species must be removed by weeding. Arable farming has resulted in a loss of biodiversity, as natural ecosystems have been replaced with mono-cultures of crop species. Pastoral farming changes natural ecosystems by removing or reducing the predators of farm animals. Their movement is restricted by keeping them in fields, barns or cages.

As populations have grown and technology advanced, farming has changed dramatically. What used to be a largely subsistence economy has become commercial and industrialised.

Ploughing sowing, weeding and harvesting, which used to be done by hand or with the aid of animals, has become mechanised. Tractors and harvesters have replaced people. Weeding has been replaced largely with the use of herbicides.

Farm animal have been bred to increase their productivity. Many traditional farm breeds have been replaced by new strains of animals bred to be more productive. These modern strains produce more meat and less fat in pigs, lay more eggs or grow faster in chickens or yield more milk and beef in cattle. Many pastoral farms regularly use doses of anti-biotics to stimulate growth and control disease.

fig.211 Combine harvester at work on a Norfolk farm

2015 farm facts

Total UK farm wrokers: **476,000**
% of UK workforce: **1.6%**
Total UK farms: **212,000**
Total areas: **183,000 km2**
Total area arable: **64,000 km2**
total area pastoral: **119,000 km2**
Average farm size: **54 hectares**
Average farmer holder: **59 years**
% of UK food needs: **59%**
Value of exports: **£14 billion**
value of imports: **£32.5 billion**
Total subsidies: **£3.19 billion**
Gross Value added: **£9.9 billion**
Total sheep numbers: **31 million**
Total cow numbers: **10 million**
Total pig numbers: **4.5 million**
Total pountry numbers: **9.6 million**

Sustainable farming?

Farming has had a significant impact on our ecosystems. Many believe that the way we grow and raise our food is not sustainable in the long-term. Farming will have to change if our farms are to remain productive.

With global populations set to rise to over 9 billion in the next few decades, can we afford to be importing 40% of our food from overseas?

Organisations like The Soil Association promote organic farming. Sustain campaigns for a better approach to food and farming. These organisations, and others, point to the damaging impact of some farming techniques.

⊙ Increased field sizes, which aids mechanisation, has led to a loss of hedgerows and increased wind-blown soil erosion.

⊙ An over-reliance on chemical fertiliser has led to a decline in soil structure and a decline in the soil organisms essential for the healthy growth of crops.

⊙ Excess run-off of fertilizers and animal waste from farms has led to the eutrophication of waterways.

⊙ The draining of marshes and wetlands for arable land has led to the loss of 95% of these valuable habitats.

⊙ Farming has become a year round process, as consumers demand crops out of season. Land can no longer be left 'fallow' to recover but must be used every year.

⊙ The regular use of anti-biotics in farm animals has led to the development of anti-biotic resistant bacteria which are now posing a serious threat to human health.

fig.212 Free-range chicken farm, Lincolnshire

Humans use, modify and change ecosystems and environments to obtain food, energy and water.

What is the impact of commercial fishing?

Britain has a long history of fishing in the fish-rich waters around the British Isles. The relatively shallow waters of the North Sea, Irish Sea and Atlantic shelf, are home to many species of **shellfish**, **pelagic fish** (mid-water migratory species, such as herring and mackerel) and **demersal fish** (bottom dwelling species such as cod, plaice and sole).

Through the 20th Century fishing techniques grew more advanced and ships grew larger. Ships with a larger tonnage could catch and process more fish at sea rather than return quickly to port to offload their catch.

Between 1887 and 1913 the total catch of fish landed in the UK **rose from 553,000 tonnes to 1.2 million tonnes.** The two World Wars disrupted fishing but it resumed in the post war years. The 953,000 tonnes landed in 1955 marked a post-war high in catches.

From the 1980s onwards, fish catches have steadily declined, with **species such as cod, haddock and whiting showing the greatest fall.**

While shellfish catches have risen slightly, the overall catch is down. 415,000 tonnes were landed in UK ports in 2015, with an additional 287,000 tonnes landed by UK ships in overseas ports.

As a member of the European Union,

▲ fig.213 **Brixham fishing boats, south coast**

fishing in EU waters is controlled by the **Common Fisheries Policy**. This agreement sets catch limits and issues licences to fish. In 2015, Britain had the third largest catch of fish among its European partners (702,000 tonnes), after Spain (902,000 tonnes) and Denmark (869,000 tonnes).

However, these figures are far behind the catches of non-EU Norway (2,146,000 tonnes) and Iceland (1,317,000 tones).

Today there are just **12,000 people employed as fishers in the UK** (working on just over 6,000 boats). This is down from 48,000 in 1948. Most of these fishers voted to leave the EU in the 2016 referendum. They see the Common Fisheries Policy as responsible for the decline of their industry.

Many ecologists blame over-fishing for the decline, especially catches by the largest, most-efficient boats. These land the majority of Britain's fish catch.

2015 Fish facts

Total UK fishers: **12,107**
Total UK vessels: **6,187**
UK tonnage: **187,371** tonnes
Total catch: **708,100** tonnes
Shellfish: **149,500** tonnes
Pelagic: **389,800** tonnes
Demersal: **168,800** tonnes
Value of catch: **£775** million
Gross Value Added: **£604** million
Net imports: **238,000** tonnes
Value of imports: **£1,336** million

Sustainable futures?

"For the fishing industry, NEF analysis shows that restoring UK fish stocks to healthy levels and promoting lower carbon emissions through quota allocation across the main UK fishing fleets would mean an extra 457,000 tonnes of fish landed each year, leading to an additional £268 million GVA (Gross Value Added) and a 24% increase in employment, the equivalent of 4,922 new jobs.

New Economics Foundation, Blue

Ecosystems under threat

Fish populations are governed by natural processes of predation, food supply and disease but they have been most severely impacted by over-fishing. Across the world it is estimated that **61% of fisheries are being exploited to their maximum healthy capacity.**

Furthermore, **29% of stocks are now over-exploited** to the point of possible 'collapse.' Collapse occurs when the breeding stock of a fish species is so depleted that it can no longer effectively reproduce itself. This happened in the **Grand Banks** fisheries off the Canadian Atlantic Coast.

In the summer of **1992 catches of cod fell to just 1% of their previous levels.** 40,000 people lost their jobs as a result.

In Britain's waters some species may be facing a similar fate. **North Sea cod and Irish Sea sole are showing reduced reproductive capacity.**

Fish, such as cod, take several years to reach breeding age. **Young fish may be caught without ever having the chance to breed.** With 40-60% of the total EU catch dumped at sea because the fish caught do not match the permitted quota, we may be fishing our waters to collapse without even eating the fish.

Commercial fishing also threatens other marine habitats. Bottom trawlers may damage deep water corals, while scallop trawlers destroy large areas of the shallow water marine bed ecosystem by dragging a net attached to a heavy metal bar across the sea bed. Other problems include the bi-catch of unwanted species, such as dolphins and

fig.214 **Small, inshore fishing trawler**

sharks, caught up in large nets.

Organisations like the **Marine Stewardship Council** encourage consumers to buy their fish from 'certified sustainable fisheries'. In 2015 there were **281 fisheries in 33 countries that were MSC certified** as sustainable. **Worldwide MSC certification accounted for 9.4% of total global fisheries.** However, with 3 billion people worldwide dependent on fish for some of their daily protein, managing fish stocks sustainably has some way to go.

71

Humans use, modify and change ecosystems and environments to obtain food, energy and water.

How do we meet our need for clean water?

The supply of water in the UK is an issue because **demand does not always match supply**. Most rain falls in the hills and mountains of the west and north (these are areas of **water surplus**) but our greatest demand for water, whether for people or industry is in the South East (an area of **water deficit**.)

Even large northern cities, such as Manchester, were built on lower-lying, flatter ground where water is hard to store in reservoirs. In the past, clean water was not abundant, especially since large rivers, such as the Irwell in Manchester, had become polluted with industrial waste and sewage.

The most common response to water shortages is to build reservoirs in the nearly mountains to collect rainwater. The water is then piped to the cities via **aqueducts**.

The map opposite shows the main aqueducts of North West England. Liverpool receives the much of its water from Lake Vyrnwy in Wales as well as from the Rivington reservoirs near Bolton. **Manchester receives most of its water from the Thirlmere and Haweswater reservoirs in the Lake District.**

In the 1890s, the Manchester Corporation **built the Thirlmere Reservoir by flooding a glacial trough** to the west of Helvellyn. The water is still piped under gravity along the 154 km-long Thirlmere Aqueduct.

As demand for water continued to grow, **Manchester built a second reservoir at Haweswater**. By raising the level of two existing lakes a new reservoir was created with a capacity of 76 million cubic metres. Today Haweswater provides **25% of the North West's water needs**. It is connected to Manchester via the 90km Haweswater Aqueduct. This aqueduct, finished in the 1950s, took 20 years to build. **Every day it pipes 570 million litres of water from Cumbria to Manchester.**

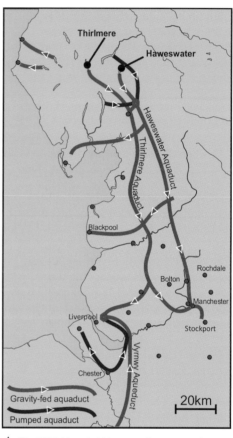

▲ Fig.207 **North West major aqueducts**

Gravity-fed aquaduct
Pumped aquaduct
20km

River to river water transfer

A second solution to water deficit is to transfer water from one river system to another. The **Ely Ouse Essex Transfer Scheme** allows water from the surplus area of north Norfolk to be transferred to the River Stour and other rivers in Essex. Here there is a deficit of water, as local catchments are unable to meet the demands of growing towns and cities.

Started in the early 1970s, the scheme **diverts water from the Great Ouse via a cut-off channel**. The water then flows south in new channels, taking it to Essex. The scheme transfers up to **455 million litres of water each day**. In dry years, this accounts for **30% of Essex's water**.

In 2014 the scheme was expanded by enlarging the Abberton reservoir near Colchester.

Fig.209 **Great Ouse cut-off channel**

▼ Fig.208 **Lake Vyrnwy, constructed 1880s**

Environmental issues

⊙ The building of **reservoirs requires the flooding of land** which could be used for farming or other uses. Sometimes villages are destroyed as was the case with the Thirlmere and Haweswater reservoirs.

⊙ While an **new habitat is created** for aquatic wildlife when creating reservoirs, other **land ecosystems may be lost**.

⊙ **Dams and reservoirs change the regime (annual flow pattern) of a river.** This can lead to a build up of sediment which may require dredging. Excess plant growth can choke a river downstream of the dam.

⊙ Moving water from one river to another can change the **chemical composition of the recipient river**. This may affect its ecology.

⊙ Rivers may be come **more saline in their lower courses** as flows are reduced.

⊙ **Non-native, invasive species** of plants and animals may be inadvertently transferred from one river basin to another creating ecological problems.

72

Humans use, modify and change ecosystems and environments to obtain food, energy and water.

How does the need for energy affect the environment?

Energy, in a scientific definition, is the capacity of a system to perform work. For us, it means we need food in order to build our cells, move around, reproduce and all the activities of life.

We get our energy from the food we eat. That energy was, in turn, taken from the Sun, either by plants that converted sunlight via photosynthesis or from animals eating the plants that had previously taken energy for the Sun. Life on earth, therefore, is dependent on solar energy in almost every respect.

However, in modern societies we think about energy in a different way. Energy is something we use to enable our machinery and vehicles to work, whether it is recharging the mobile phone or sending a rocket into space.

Since our machines can't eat food the way we do, we supply them with energy from the other forms we find in the natural world. We use natural gas to heat our homes or cook our food, oil to power our cars and lorries.

Modern life is dependent on the use of electricity. This is not energy in itself but the way we have learned to move energy from one place to another: from the power plants where it is generated to the home or factory where it is used.

In the next section we will look at the different types of energy we use in our society in more detail.

Wind farms and the environment

▲ fig.218 Offshore windfarm

Wind is a renewable energy source (see page 79) which has been used by humans for thousands of years, for pumping water and to grind corn into flour. Today we use wind turbines to generate electricity. Wind farms are sites of multiple turbines on land or out at sea. In the UK the majority of our wind farms on onshore but more are being built at sea.

On land, each turbine has a small footprint (just a few square metres) so the land can be used for other purposes. The big environmental advantage for wind power is that it produces none of the greenhouse gases that contribute to climate change, except in the manufacture and construction of the turbines themselves.

Some people think turbines are ugly and spoil the landscape or the view out to sea. Others disagree thinking that the turbines look attractive. Some complain of the noise turbines make. Others fear that offshore farms may disturb the migratory patterns of birds.

Fracking and the environment

'Fracking' (see page 82) is a method used to extract oil and gas from underground rock structures. In the USA in 2015 almost half of the oil and gas was extracted using fracking technology. While the gas produced from fracking creates less carbon dioxide when burned than coal, it is still a fossil fuel and so its burning will release more greenhouse gases to the atmosphere.

▲ fig.219 Fracking site in USA

Fracking involves pumping highly pressurised water into the bedrock. This can create large quantities of contaminated waste water which must be treated. Some fear this may contaminate local water supplies.

There is some evidence that fracking may lead to minor earth tremors. However, these are very small events compared to natural earthquakes. Local residents close to fracking sites complain of traffic congestion in narrow country lanes. They also fear the visual impact of the fracking wells in the landscape.

Thinking it through

1. What is meant by the term ecosystem? (1)

2. Outline how humans have changed the environment in these islands over the last few thousand years? (3)

3.

4. Where is the source of most of Manchester's clean water? (1)

5. Outline some of the possible environmental problems associated with river to river water transfer schemes. (4)

6. Outline how commercial fishing can impact on ecosystems. (4)

7. Suggest reasons why it is important for people to harvest fish in a sustainable way. (4)

8. Outline the positive and negative environmental impacts of wind power. (4)

9. "Human's have both positive and negative impacts on ecosystems and the environment." Using examples, discuss this view. (8)

fig.220 Electricity pylons: an eyesore whatever the energy source

Humans use, modify and change ecosystems and environments to obtain food, energy and water.

What is renewable and non-renewable energy?

There are numerous sources of energy on Earth that we can use. We can divide these energy resources into two main groups: renewable and non-renewable.

Renewable resources are those that present a continuous or near continuous stream of energy which we can utilise. These renewables include solar, wind, waves, geothermal, hydro-electric, biogas and other biofuels.

Most renewables are powered by the Sun. However, geothermal relies on energy generated by nuclear reactions deep in the Earth's core and tidal power relies on the gravitational pull of the moon (as well as the Sun).

These sources of energy should be around for many years to come. The Sun has perhaps four or more billion years left to burn and the moon is moving away from Earth only very, very slowly.

Non-renewable energy resources are ones that can only be used once. To paraphrase a popular supermarket sales pitch, 'Once it's gone, it's gone!'

The non-renewables

The three most common non-renewable resources are the fossil fuels: **coal, oil and natural gas.** These are the fossilised remains of ancient forests (coal) and sea creatures (oil and gas) that have been converted over millions of years into rich sources of hydrocarbons. **We can burn these fuels releasing the solar energy they absorbed from the Sun millions of years ago.**

The problem is that once we burn them they are gone for good. There are two other sources of fuel that should be consid-

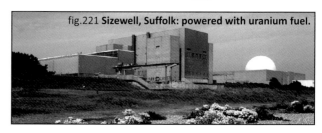

fig.221 **Sizewell, Suffolk: powered with uranium fuel.**

ered as non-renewable. The first is the **uranium** that goes to fuel nuclear power stations. This is a finite resource because the fuel decays in the reactor (see page 78.)

The second is the unsustainable burning of **fuelwood**, where no replacement trees are planted. Only by replanting forests can wood be sustainable.

Industrial societies have developed over the last two century by the mass exploitation of fossil fuels. First coal was used during the industrial revolution – and is still widely used across the world. Then, with the invention of the internal combustion engine, oil became the main fuel used for transport.

As a global system of trade and travel developed, oil became more essential to (literally) keep the wheels turning. We have seen in section 1.2.1 how oil, and its refined bi-products, is still a large part of the trade that Britain does with the rest of the world.

Burning natural gas has expanded greatly as it is a much cleaner fuel than coal and pollutes far less. As counties develop they are able to build the complex infrastructure needed to store of transport this highly flammable gas around the country and into people's homes.

Fossil fuels have been so successful because they are a highly concentrated source of energy. The geological processes that produced them have concentrated the energy within to create 'super fuels.'

As fossil fuels are the result of carbon life forms being concentrated by time and pressure, they cannot be replaced in the human time scales. Secondly, the environmental conditions for the formation of coal and oil, found million of years ago on Earth, do not exist today.

In short, fossil fuels are running out.

▼ fig.222 **The most important non-renewable energy sources.**

Coal. Coal is a combustible, sedimentary rock. It is the fossilised remains of plant material converted from peat into coal over millions of years. At a rough estimate a 100 metre thick layer of peat, and the energy the plants took from the Sun when growing, is compressed into just one metre of coal. It is the world's most important source of energy for generating electricity.

Petroleum. Petroleum is another fossil fuel. In its naturally occurring state it is often referred to as crude oil. Petroleum is the remains of plankton and algae buried on the sea bed under sedimentary rocks. Over millions of years these are converted in hydrocarbon chains producing compounds such as petrol and diesel. The world uses about 15 billion litres of oil each day.

Natural Gas. Another fossil fuel, natural gas is composed mostly of methane. It is produced under temperature and pressure from buried organic matter and is often found close to oil fields. Natural gas burns cleanly to leave just water and carbon dioxide. The burning of natural gas is adding to CO_2 levels in the atmosphere. Each year the world burns around 3,400km^3 of gas.

Uranium. Uranium is the fuel used to power nuclear fission plants. Like fossil fuels it is non-renewable as uranium fuel break down into other elements as they release their energy. One of those elements, plutonium, can be used for further fission. However, plutonium is highly radioactive and toxic. Currently the world uses about 63,000 tonnes of uranium each year.

▼ fig.223 **North Sea gas rig is battered by storms.**

How are fossil fuels contributing to climate change?

A major environmental problem is associated with the bi-products of burning fossil fuels. The living things which were converted into coal, oil and natural gas, took their energy for the sun by photosynthesis. Prehistoric plants combined the energy of photons (packets of solar energy in sunlight) with water and carbon dioxide to create glucose and then more complex molecules.

As we burn fossil fuels, the water and carbon dioxide, combined many million years ago, are released as waste gases. The water is no problem. It simply rains out of the atmosphere and rejoins the water cycle.

Since the Industrial Revolution, the concentration of atmospheric carbon dioxide has risen from around 280 parts per million to around 404 ppm at the start of 2017. This is leading to a warming of the atmosphere where carbon dioxide acts as a greenhouse gas, trapping heat and leading to a slow but steady rise in global temperatures.

fig.224 **Traffic on the M25.**

It's not just the carbon dioxide

The rather inconvenient truth is that while fossil fuels are a brilliant source of energy, they are also threatening to over-heat our planet with possibly catastrophic consequences for life.

Another problem with fossil fuels is the other elements found within them. After all, they weren't designed as fuels but are just very old compressed and chemically-altered dead things. The worst culprit is coal which contains sulphur within it. **When burnt coal releases sulphur dioxide. This gas can then dissolve in cloud droplets to fall as sulphuric acid.**

The chemicals released by burning fuels, along with the tiny particles of soot released from engines, can help to create a problem called **photochemical smog**. Under certain weather conditions, these smogs can be seen developing over large cities, including Manchester and London. They can cause serious health problems, such as asthma, as well as damage buildings and wildlife.

Britain is heavily dependent on fossil fuels, especially oil for transport and gas for domestic use and electricity generation. Britain's 'dirty' coal fired power stations are being phased out under environmental laws, but however 'clean' the burning, fossil fuels will still emit carbon dioxide. **It is this carbon dioxide which is responsible, along with other gases such as** methane and the nitrous oxides, for global warming.

This is why many climate scientists believe that the world as a whole must quickly phase out almost all our use of fossil fuels, and by 2050 at the latest.

Since Britain uses, on average, two thirds more energy per person than the global average, and over twelve times more than Bangladesh, many people believe that our country has a duty to move further and faster in reducing our use of fossil fuels.

Conflict over fossil fuels - past, present, future

Much of the world's oil is located in the very unstable region of the world known as the Middle East. Russia has the planet's largest known natural gas reserves. Many people believe that it is foolish to rely on energy resources that come from regions that are unstable or from countries where the government may not see eye to eye with our own government, such as Russia.

Many believe that the 1992 Gulf War and 2003 Iraq War were linked to control of Iraq's large oil reserves. Others claim that our desire to buy cheap oil from Saudi Arabia and the Gulf states means our governments turn a blind eye to appalling human rights abuses in those countries.

In 2015 the 'Islamic State' was able to take control of large areas or Iraq and Syria. In doing so it was able to access the oil wells of the regions it captured. Oil then found its way onto the international markets via smuggling routes, further funding the terrorist network.

As fossil fuels become more scarce the price is likely to rise. This makes the exploitation of less easily accessible reserves more economically viable.

fig.225 **Oil fire in Iraq war zone**

This is going to mean more conflicts between energy firms, who want to make profits, and environmentalists, who want the fuels left in the ground. In the coming years there will be **big debates about 'fracking'** as well as oil and gas extraction in Alaska and the Great Australian Bight. Plans to extract more oil from Canada's 'tar sands' will be controversial.

> "Decades of oil-hungry backing for despots, from Iran to Oman, Egypt to Saudi Arabia, fuelled first the rise of Islamism and then the eruption of Al-Qaida-style terror more than a decade ago." *The Guardian, 2010.*

What are the sources of renewable energy?

As the name implies **renewable energy sources are those which can be used over and over again**. Hydro Electric Power (HEP) is renewable because rainfall with refill the reservoirs behind a dam. Solar energy is renewable as the Sun will definitely rise again tomorrow morning. The tides will continue to ebb and flow as long as the Moon orbits the Earth.

For those worried about climate change, the greatest advantage of renewables is that they **put less carbon dioxide into the atmosphere than fossil fuels**. That is not to say that these energy sources are carbon-free: they all result in some carbon being released whether from the energy used in manufacture of the machinery involved or the concrete used in the dams or power plants. Large HEP dams in the lower courses

▼ fig.227 **The most important renewable energy sources.**

Wind. Britain has great potential for developing wind power further. In 2016 there were 5733 onshore turbines and 1465 turbines offshore. These had the capacity to supply almost 10 million homes. However, the biggest problem with the wind is its intermittent nature. Turbines tend to produce just a quarter of their potential as the wind doesn't blow all the time.

Hydro (HEP). HEP uses the gravitational energy of water held behind a dam to generate electricity. HEP provided Britain with about 5,000 GWh of electricity in 2016. A further 4,100 GWh of energy came from four pumped storage stations. Here water is pumped up to a reservoir using cheaper off-peak electricity. It is then released to generate power at times of peak demand.

Solar. in 2016, despite being rather cloudy, Britain had the sixth greatest amount of installed solar capacity on the planet. Photo-voltaic panels convert sunlight to electricity. In the six summer months of 2016 solar produced more electricity (6,964 GWh) in the UK than did coal (6,342 GWh). Government subsidies to solar have been cut which has slowed growth of this energy industry.

Geothermal. This takes heat from deep underground and uses it to produce electricity as well as heat homes and other buildings. Despite not being volcanic, like Iceland, Britain has many sources of underground heat. A 2012 report suggested geothermal could produce 20% of UK electricity, equivalent to nine nuclear power stations, as well as heat millions of homes.

Biomass. Anaerobic digestion is a process by which organic matter breaks down, in the absence of oxygen, to produce methane. This process make gas from sewage and agricultural waste. Incineration of waste can also be used in thermal power plants to generate electricity. The DRAX power station is being converted to run on wood pellets rather than coal.

Tidal. Britain has some of the highest tidal ranges on the planet. There is great potential to harness the tides to generate power. Tides may not run all day long but they are very predictable. Tidal energy could produce up to 20% of Britain's electricity but it is still in its infancy. Plans have been announced to build a barrage in Swansea Bay and a tidal array is being built in the Pentland Firth.

fig.226 **Oil-seed rape can be used to create a biofuel.**

of rivers are especially problematic as they require relatively wide dams requiring vast quantities of concrete.

The biggest drawback for **renewables is that they cannot be relied on 24 hours a day.** The sun doesn't shine at night, the tides only ebb and flood twice a day, the rain doesn't fall everyday and the wind doesn't blow constantly. This means, it is argued, that human societies will need to use fossil fuels and nuclear power for the foreseeable future.

Another argument against renewables is their expense. At present renewables are, on average, much more expensive to use than coal or gas. Supporters of renewables point to the rapidly reducing cost of these industries which are relatively new on the global scene. They point to the **70% reduction in the price of solar panels since 2010.** They argue that if the money that has already been spent on fossil fuels and nuclear was to be spent on renewable technology then the prices would plummet.

At present the biggest barrier to expanding renewable energy use is the almost 100% dominance of petrol, diesel and kerosene used in road, sea and air transportation. in addition, with the exception of pump storage reservoirs, there is currently no mechanism for the mass storage of electricity. Once these problems has been solved fossil fuels can be rapidly phased out. An end to burning fossil fuels would see natural processes once again determine the stores and transfers in the carbon cycle.

fig.228 **Jack-up vessel used for the construction of offshore wind farms.**

There are a range of energy sources available to the UK.

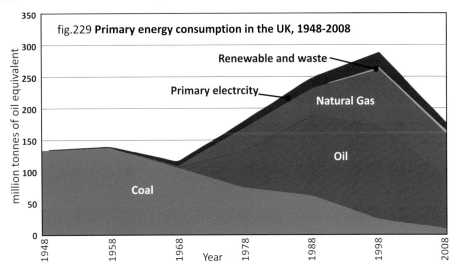

How has the energy mix changed in the UK?

The energy mix describes the variety of sources of energy a country uses to meet its demand.

Over the years, the energy mix in the UK has changed dramatically. Figure 229 shows the primary energy consumption for the UK from just after World War Two until 2008. **Energy consumption rose rapidly from the 1960s as electrical devices became more widespread in the home and car ownership expanded.** Since the late 1990s consumption has fallen as a result of energy efficiency.

In the **1940s and 1950s the principal source of energy was coal.** From the 1960s this was added to by oil and natural gas, as well as some HEP and nuclear (referred to in figure 229 as primary electricity). From the 1980s waste incineration and biomass began to add a little to the energy mix.

The advance of renewable technologies has further diversified the energy mix. The decline in primary electricity seen from 1998, which was the result of old nuclear power stations being closed, has been reversed by the growth of renewable electricity generation, especially from wind.

Figure 230 shows how the percentages have changed since 1971. The big growth has been in natural gas which has mostly replaced coal.

fig.229 **Primary energy consumption in the UK, 1948-2008**

million tonnes of oil equivalent

Renewable and waste
Primary electrcity
Natural Gas
Oil
Coal

Year: 1948, 1958, 1968, 1978, 1988, 1998, 2008

▼ fig.230 **Primary energy consumption in the UK, 1971 and 2016**

1971 | 2016

Coal
Natural gas
Petroleum
Nuclear
Hydro & wind
Bioenergy & waste
Imported electrcity

What does the future hold?

The future energy mix of the UK will depend on many factors. These could be economic, environmental or political. However, it could also be a technological question.

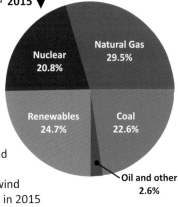

fig.231 **How cool are electric cars?**

A very large part of the energy mix is energy for transport. **Currently most transport in the UK relies on fossil fuels to power cars, lorries, ships, planes and trains.** While it has proved relatively easy, if expensive, to electrify railways, fossil fuels still lead the way in most engines. Electric hybrid cars still rely on their oil-powered internal combustion engines and, as yet, we have no other commercially viable ways of fuelling aeroplanes or ships other than by using petroleum.

So the energy mix may be decided, not by politicians or environmentalists, but by engineers and scientists. Can electric cars be made faster to charge? It is possible to power a car using a hydrogen fuel cell, but in 2015 there were just twelve hydrogen refuelling stations in the whole of the USA.

Electricty generation in the mix

Fig.232 shows how the UK's electricity was generated in 2015. The big change on previous decades is in the percentage of coming from **renewables**.

Overall, renewable electricity generation in 2015 stood at 83.3TWh - an increase of 29% on 2014. Offshore wind generation rose by 30% and onshore wind by 24%. This was due to increased capacity and high wind speeds. Average wind speeds in 2015 were the highest in the past 15 years. Hydro-electricity generation rose by 7.4% compared to the previous year, while generation from bio-energy was up by 28% from 2015.

fig.232 **UK Electricity generation** 2015 ▼

Nuclear 20.8%
Natural Gas 29.5%
Renewables 24.7%
Coal 22.6%
Oil and other 2.6%

Juliet Davenport, from renewable energy company Good Energy, said: "Yet again renewables are really proving their worth and it's fantastic to see record amounts of electricity generated by renewable sources. Renewables . . . are leading the way when it comes to making the UK more energy secure in the future."

What are the benefits and problems of nuclear power?

Nuclear power describes the method of generating electricity from the heat generated by reactions in the nuclei of atoms. It is the most controversial of all the sources of energy we use on the planet.

In 2015 there were 437 fission reactors operating in 31 countries. These accounted for 11% of global electricity production. In the UK there are currently 15 reactors producing around 21% of the UK electricity production.

Many of these reactors are nearing the end of their lives and nuclear production of electricity is expected to fall by half by 2025.

In 2016 EDF, the French energy company, agreed to build a new nuclear power station at Hinkley Point in Somerset. With the aid of investment from the Chinese nuclear company CGN, Hinkley C plant will be the first new nuclear power station built in Britain since Sizewell B, which opened in 1996.

EDF expect the plant, with its two pressurised water reactors, to be operational by 2026. The plant will cost an estimated £18 billion (or £24.5 billion with financing).

To ensure the deal with EDF and CGN went ahead the British government guaranteed a higher 'strike price' for the electricity to be paid for 35 years. An estimate by the National Audit Office calculated that this inflated price will mean British consumers paying an extra £29.7 billion over the lifetime of the power plant.

Reactor currently generating electricity

Decommissioned reactor no longer generating electricity

Possible site for new power station

Dounreay
Torness
Hunterston
Chapelcross
Hartlepool
Sellafield
Heysham
Wylfa
Trawsfynndd
Sizewell
Berkeley
Bradwell
Oldbury
Hinkley Point
Dungeness

▲ fig.233 **UK nuclear power stations**

▼ fig.234 **Anti-nuclear protest, Hinkley**

The science behind the power

The fuel in a nuclear fission reactor is enriched uranium. The enrichment increases the concentration of the U-235 isotope. This isotope is fissile, which means that its nucleus can be easily split releasing vast quantity of energy. A kilogram of uranium can release the equivalent energy of burning 2-3 million kilograms of coal.

During a nuclear reaction neutrons are released which can split further atoms. These atoms, in turn, release more neutrons, creating a **chain reaction.**

In a nuclear bomb this process is uncontrolled. However, **in a nuclear reactor, water or graphic is used to absorb excess neutrons and control the speed of the reaction.** A coolant flows through the reactor and this coolant transfers its heat to water into steam. This steam then turns a turbine generating electricity.

Why is nuclear power controversial?

Those in favour of nuclear power point to its **good safety record across the world**. For all the plants in operation, now and in the past, there have not been many nuclear accidents. **Nuclear power is also excellent at providing 'base load' electricity**; the essential underpinning of power needed to run a national grid. They point to the impossibility of wind power to do the same.

Once built, nuclear power stations can generate electricity for decades. **Supporters point to the low carbon emissions of** **nuclear power, which some estimates have rated as similar to wind turbines.**

Ppponents of nuclear power point to the potential for **truly catastrophic accidents, such as Chernobyl in 1986**. They worry about the potential for the plutonium generated in the reactors to be used for nuclear weapons or for nuclear waste to find itself in a terrorist 'dirty bomb'.

Opponents point to **problems nuclear waste** which must be stored safely and securely for thousands of years. The half life

of plutonium-239 is around 24,000 years - twice the length of existing human civilisation. Many say the money spent on nuclear would be **better spent on renewable energies**, which don't leave the clean up to future generations.

Accidents do happen.

Nuclear power has a generally good safety record, but **when accidents happen they can be devastating.** The worst nuclear accident happened at Chernobyl, Ukraine in 1986. Here the reactor suffered a devastating **'meltdown'**. Radiation was spread across much of Ukraine, Russia and Europe. Estimates predict that up to 40,000 extra cases of cancer will be caused by the disaster. In 2011, a tsunami damaged the power station at Fukushima Daiichi, Japan, causing 'meltdowns' in three reactors.

fig.235 **Chernobyl, Ukraine, 2103.** The 'New Safe Confinement' (NSC) structure can be seen at the left. The NSC will seal in the damaged reactor for the next 100 years, but at a cost of €1.5 billion.

Energy in the UK is affected by a number of factors and requires careful management and consideration of future supplies.

How do we generate electricity from the wind?

The UK is uniquely placed to benefit from an increase in the use of renewable energy. While we may not be the sunniest country on Earth we do have the capacity to generate significant amount of energy from the Sun. More importantly, we also have a **particularly windy location** on the western edge of Europe. Britain has Europe's greatest number of potential sites for both onshore and offshore wind farms. Some people put the figure as high as **40% of all European sites.**

How does a wind turbine work?

A wind turbine acts like an enormous aeroplane propeller, working in reverse. At the top of the tower, which is usually between 25 and 75 metres high, sits the rotor and the blades. Usually there are three

fig.236 **Sheringham Shoal Offshore Wind Farm**

blades made from fibreglass and reinforced polyester or a wood-epoxy mix. They range in length up to 80m. As the wind blows through the blades it turns the rotor just like in a traditional windmill.

Once moving the blades turn at a regular rotation of 10-30 revolutions per minute. A sensor detects the wind speed and direction and a 'yaw mechanism' turns the blades to keep facing the wind. The rotational movement of the rotor is speeded up through a series of gears. **A generator converts the rotation into electricity.**

The amount of electricity the turbine can generate is dependent on the speed and duration of the wind and the size of the turbine. **Turbines are described by their maximum power generation capacity.** A large turbine may be rated as 5 MegaWatts with new super-turbines rated at

8MW.

However, this rating does not mean that this is what the turbine will actually generate. The wind may not blow and wind speeds vary considerably throughout the day and year. Turbines are also switched off during very strong winds to prevent damage. **In Britain, wind turbines generate at around 28% of their full capacity.** Offshore is more efficient (35%) as the wind is more steady. Onshore turbines generate at around 25% of capacity.

By the end of 2015 there were 951 wind generation projects in the UK with 6691 turbines. Of these 1465 were offshore, the rest on land. It is estimated that these turbines generated some 34 million MWh of electricity in 2015 or enough to power over **8 million homes.**

You can check the current figures for wind turbines and their generation capacity at **www.renewableuk.com.**

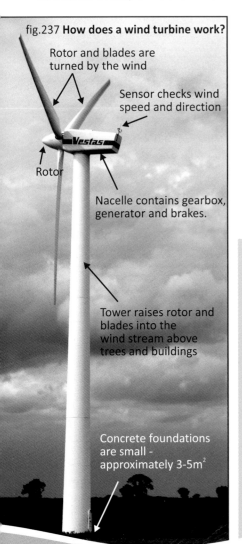

fig.237 **How does a wind turbine work?**

Rotor and blades are turned by the wind

Sensor checks wind speed and direction

Vestas

Rotor

Nacelle contains gearbox, generator and brakes.

Tower raises rotor and blades into the wind stream above trees and buildings

Concrete foundations are small - approximately 3-5m²

Graceful sight or eyesore?

With so many possible sites for wind farms, why isn't Britain the European leader for wind generation?

While lots of people consider wind turbines to be elegant and graceful, many people consider them an eyesore which should not be allowed to spread across our countryside.

As a result many **applications for wind farms are rejected by the local council during planning**. Permissions granted by the councils may be overturned by the government on appeal. Offshore wind farms have fewer objectors but they cost around 50% more to build than on land.

Wind power in Europe

In 2015 Britain had the **third largest installed capacity for onshore wind generation in Europe** with 13,600MW. Germany had 45,000MW and Spain 23,000MW of installed capacity.

However, **when compared to the size of the population, Britain slipped down the table to 9th place** - below the European average. While Denmark produced 894 watts per person from wind, followed by Sweden (618 W/person), Germany (553 W/person) and Ireland (537 W/person), **Britain produced 210 W/person**, just above the figure for Estonia, Greece and Belgium.

Energy in the UK is affected by a number of factors and requires careful management and consideration of future supplies.

Could the UK expand the use of solar and hydro?

Electricity generation usually relies on turning a generator at high speed to create a flow of electrons along a wire. In conventional thermal power stations fossil fuels are burned to heat water into steam. The steam then turns a turbine which turns the generator. In nuclear power the heat generated by nuclear fission is used to heat a gas, such as chlorine, which in turn heats the water.

In wind power it is the rotor blades which spin the generator. In hydro-electric power it is the movement of the water released from behind the dam which moves the turbines connected to the generator. In some large-scale solar projects, such as the PS10 in Spain, there is a similar transfer of heat to create steam to drive a turbine.

How do solar panels work?

The solar panels, called photo-voltaics, we see on the roofs of houses are different. They are able to convert sunlight directly into electricity.

The solar cells are based on the same technology that allows our computers or mobile phones to work: the semi-conductor or 'silicon chip'. In fact, the first generation of solar panels were made using poor quality semi-conductors rejected by the computer industry.

In a solar cell the photo-voltaic surface absorbs photons, which are packets of solar energy. The photons disturb the arrangement of electrons within the atomic layers of the solar cell, creating an electrical current.

The first generation of solar cells were not very efficient. They only

fig.238 **Solar panels on house roof.**

produced a fraction of the electricity compared to the photon energy falling onto the cell.

The second generation of photo-voltaics used a different combination of elements built up in a thin film. They generate around 13% of the photon energy falling on their surface. These thin-film panels have brought down the cost of solar power. They are no longer reliant on the waste products of the computer industry.

A third generation of PV panels are likely to use a system which concentrates solar energy onto cells that are able to extract the energy from all the different colours of sunlight. **These could operate at over 40% efficiency. They could transform solar energy in the future.**

There are a number of issues associated with solar power which will need to be addressed if it is to continue to increase its contribution to the UK energy mix.

⊙ Since power cannot be generated at night when energy is still needed **storage systems are needed to allow electricity**

generated in the day to be used at night. Currently home batteries are very large and expensive. However, peak electricity demand is usually during the middle of the day when solar generation is at its peak.

⊙ **Winter solar generation is significantly lower in the UK compared to summer** because of the shorter days and lower angle of the sun in the sky. So summer solar will need a replacement during winter months.

⊙ **There are millions of potential solar sites in the UK on the roofs of private homes** but most people cannot afford the thousands of pounds needed to fit solar panels. In recent years, government subsidies have been cut for solar. Community-owned power co-operatives could help but, unlike Germany, such co-ops are not common here.

⊙ **Solar farms can sometimes be denied planning permission by councils.** These disputes will need to be resolved if large-scale solar farms are to expand.

fig.240 **Solar panels on solar farm**

fig.241 **Pitlochry HEP dam and its fish ladder, Scotland**

Could HEP generate more?

There are enough potential sites in the UK to expand our current HEP capacity by up to 160%. This could help create the installed capacity to supply electricity when the sun isn't shining and the wind isn't blowing. However, this expansion would result in many more large-scale dams, with potential negative environmental consequences. **Dams on rivers disrupt river flow regimes** and can lead to changes in sediment transportation. **Dams can block access to migratory fish**, such a salmon, unless fitted with fish ladders.

More pump-storage projects, such as Loch Awe in Scotland and Dinorwic in Wales, could help convert solar and wind energy, generated at peak production times, into stored potential energy to be released when needed.

Energy in the UK is affected by a number of factors and requires careful management and consideration of future supplies.

What is 'fracking' and is it a good or bad idea?

Fracking, or hydraulic fracturing to use its full name, is the process by which **water and other material is injected at high pressure into gas-bearing rock with the aim of releasing the gas.**

In recent years 'fracking' has become widespread in the United States where it is used to release natural gas trapped in shales (a sedimentary rock formed from deposited mud).

In 2016 two thirds of natural gas in the USA came from fracking operations. The process has changed the energy economy of the United States by allowing access to large quantities of gas. **Some suggest that there is enough to make the USA self-sufficient in gas for the next 100 years.**

How does fracking work?

Fracking is not a new process. It has been used in the North Sea gas and oil fields for many years. It is only recently that it has become controversial as the new 'fracking' wells will be on land. The target of the process is the release of shale gas that is currently trapped in deep layers of sedimentary rock far

fig.242 **A hydraulic fracturing operation at a Marcellus Shale well in the USA**

below the surface.

Hydraulic fracturing involves boring deep wells often several kilometres below the surface and then drilling horizontally through the gas-bearing shales. **A mixture of water and proppants plus a few other chemicals is pumped down the well at high pressure.** This pressurised water cracks, or fractures, the rock. The proppants then keep the fractures open. Once the water pressure is reduced the gas is

released from the rock and it flows up the well to the surface. The water used in the process is usually shored in an open pit until it can be removed to a treatment plant. The gas is transferred to a storage facility and then added to the gas in the national grid.

At the time of publication (2017) there was no commercial-scale fracking on the British mainland. You should check to see if this is still true.

fig.243 **What might drilling for shale gas look like?**
Infographic from the Department for Business, Energy & Industrial Strategy

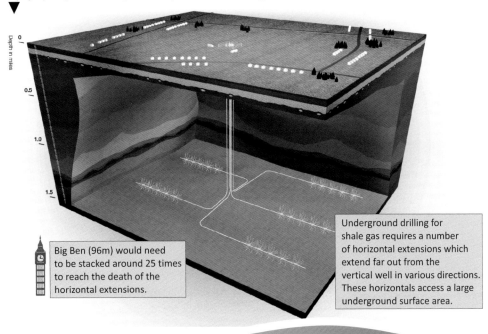

Depth in miles

0

0.5

1.0

1.5

Big Ben (96m) would need to be stacked around 25 times to reach the death of the horizontal extensions.

Underground drilling for shale gas requires a number of horizontal extensions which extend far out from the vertical well in various directions. These horizontals access a large underground surface area.

KEY TERMS

Chemical additive: chemicals, such as hydrochloric acid, added in small quantities to fracturing water to aid the process of gas release.

Hydraulic Fracturing (fracking): using high pressure water to release methane gas held in rocks, often shales, deep underground.

Proppant: sand grains or tiny artificial pellets used to keep open the fractures in the gas bearing rock.

Shale gas: sometimes referred to as 'tight gas' as this is methane held tightly between the grains of sedimentary mudstones. It can only be extracted commercially using 'fracking'.

Well: deep holes bored first vertically, then horizontally to release the shale gas

Energy in the UK is affected by a number of factors and requires careful management and consideration of future supplies.

To frack or not to frack? That is the question.

Fracking in the UK is extremely controversial. Climatologists have estimated that burning one third of the known reserves of coal, gas and oil over the next 30 years will result in catastrophic climate change. Fracking allows access to even greater reserves of gas. Burning this will inevitably lead to **more global warming**. For many this is enough to oppose fracking.

Others object to fracking as the **drilling rigs may become an eyesore in picturesque rural villages**. Some fear that the fracking process may **contaminate underground water sources** with toxic chemicals. Methane from the wells, that might escape to the surface, could also **add to greenhouse gases**.

After a minor earthquake in 2011, test fracking was halted in the UK. Government reports have since said

The case against fracking

"CO₂ concentrations haven't been this high in millions of years. Even more alarming is the rate of increase in the last five decades and the fact that CO_2 stays in the atmosphere for hundreds or thousands of years. This milestone is a wakeup call that our actions in response to climate change need to match the persistent rise in CO_2. Climate change is a threat to life on Earth and we can no longer afford to be spectators."

Dr. Erika Podest, Carbon and water cycle research scientist

that although there is a risk of minor earthquakes they are so small as to be a danger on the surface. **Anti-fracking campaigners are not convinced.**

Those opposed to fracking point out that the gas we need to ensure electricity generation 'when the sun doesn't shine and the wind doesn't blow' could be met from biogas. This can be made from the anaerobic digestion of agricultural and food waste, rubbish and sewage.

Much of the methane produced by the rotting of this waste currently ends up as a greenhouse gas in the atmosphere. Creating biogas, and burning this in stead of a fossil fuel, will still produce carbon dioxide. However, in this case the CO_2 would be part of a living carbon cycle and not act to increase atmospheric CO_2.

The British government is in favour of fracking and has proposed incentives to local communities.

These incentives allow councils to keep 100% of the business rate that a fracking business would pay, plus 1% of the total revenues from the fracking itself. Communities will also receive £100,000 when a test well is dug in their area.

Opponents say that this is no more than a 'bribe' to councils which are facing opposition to fracking from their residents but are also having to make cuts to local services as government

The case for fracking

"The anti-fracking lobby seem to think there is a bottomless pit of bill-payers' money to fund renewable energy generation. There isn't, and even if there was, we would still need gas – as a reliable source of electricity when the sun doesn't shine or the wind doesn't blow.

"In 2003, we were a net exporter of gas. By 2030 we expect to be importing close to 75% of the gas we consume. By making the most of our home-grown gas we can safeguard our own domestic supply whilst also cutting our carbon emissions."

Department of Energy and Climate Change, September 2015

grants are cut.

In 2016 fracking pilots were approved in both Lanchasire and Yorkshire despite local opposition. The Communities Secretary, Sajid Javid overturned a decision by Lanchasire County Council to deny planning permission for a test well to gas firm Cuadrilla. Supporting the appeal the minister said **"When it comes to the financial benefits of shale, our plans mean local communities benefit first."**

In response, Friends of the Earth campaigner Pollyanna Steiner said: **"Fracking goes against everything we need to do to tackle climate change. The government must end its fixation with dirty fossil fuels and focus instead on harnessing the UK's huge renewable energy resource."**

Thinking it through

1. What is meant by the term **fossil fuels**? (2)

2. Distinguish between **renewable and non-renewable** resources. (2)

3. Why is **nuclear power** a non-renewable energy source? (2)

4. Why are **fossil fuels** so important to the economies of **advanced countries**. (4)

5. Outline the **environmental effects of burning fossil fuels**. (4)

6. Outline how **conflicts can affect the cost and availability** of fossil fuels. (4)

7. Describe the types of **renewable energy** available in the UK. (4)

8. Outline the **advantages and**

▼ fig.244 **UK Anti-fracking protest.**

disadvantages of wind as an energy source. (4)

9. With reference to fig.229 describe the changes in the **UK primary energy mix** since 1948. (4)

10. Explain why **petroleum** is still so important to the **UK energy mix**. (4)

11. With reference to fig.232 explain why the UK electricity production **energy mix is described as 'balanced.'**

12. What is **nuclear power** and why is it such a **controversial** energy source? (4)

13. With reference to fig.233, describe the distribution of Britain's **nuclear power stations**. (3)

14. Why is the geography of the UK ideal for **generating electricity from wind**? (3)

15. Outline **two problems associated with solar power** in the UK. (4)

16. What is meant by **'fracking'**? (2)

17. State **one argument for and one against fracking** for shale gas in the UK. (2)

18. Outline arguments **for and against using natural gas** to generate electricity. (4)

82

Energy in the UK is affected by a number of factors and requires careful management and consideration of future supplies.

Can the UK become more sustainable in energy use?

The United Kingdom uses a broad range of energy sources, although they are still dominated by fossil fuels. In electricity production the energy mix is even more balanced. The general convention is that **a balanced energy mix is a good thing** as it doesn't leave a country vulnerable to unexpected price changes or changing environmental conditions, such as wind speeds.

However, **is a 'balanced energy mix' sustainable?** By definition the **use of fossil fuels is not sustainable** as these fuels can only be used once. Any policy that relies on fossil fuels is going to run into trouble as future supplies dwindle.

Figure 245 shows how **Britain has become dependent on the importing of natural gas.** At the start of this century Britain was a net exporter of gas. Today the UK imports far more gas than we export. Three quarters of this gas comes from just two countries – Norway (by pipe) and Qatar (by tanker as LNG, liquefied natural gas). Around two thirds of the gas we burn in the UK is used in domestic homes and to generate electricity. Even with significant exploitation of fracking, we will still eventually run out of gas.

All fossil fuels are a short-term source of energy. If Britain is to hit its carbon emission reduction targets, as well as provide long-term energy security, renewables must become even more central to our energy mix.

Energy efficiency will become very important if we are

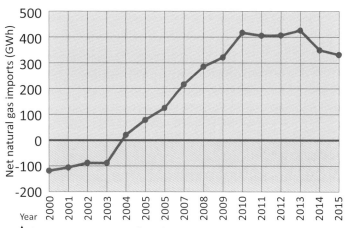

▲ fig.245 **UK net natural gas imports 2000-2015**

not to waste large amounts of precious and polluting fossil fuels.

A 2015 report, called *Less Waste, More Growth*, suggested that the **UK wastes 54% of the electricity it produces; the equivalent output of 39 nuclear power stations.**

Dr Douglas Parr, Policy Director at Greenpeace UK, commented: *"Cutting energy waste wherever possible should be a no-brainer. You can lower energy bills, cut carbon emissions, and boost energy security at a single stroke. Whatever our differences on clean energy, the Government must surely realise the obvious benefits of making our energy system more efficient."*

Local projects could help the UK become more sustainable in energy use

▲ fig.246 **BedZED has environmentally-friendly housing**

Building carbon-neutral housing.

The award-winning **Beddington Zero Energy Development** (BedZED) is a environmentally friendly housing development in Hackbridge, London. **The 82 houses are designed to run on solar power and other renewables generated on site**. They benefit from 'solar gain': the heat collected through the south-facing, triple glazed windows.

Car parking is limited, and electric cars have priority. This aims to encourage cycling and the use of public transport. **Rainwater falling on the roofs is re-used.**

In 2003, residents were using less energy than the national average. Heating requirements were 88% less than average and hot-water consumption was 57% less. The electrical power used was 25% less than the UK average.

▲ fig.247 **Southampton uses geothermal power.**

Heating & power from geothermal

Southampton City Council took the decision to create the **UK's first geothermal power scheme** in the 1980s, taking over a pilot geothermal project from the government. At the time the council wanted to make the Southampton a 'self-sustaining city' in energy generation.

Water is pumped to a depth of 1,800 metres in the Wessex Basin aquifer where it is warmed by the naturally occurring heat to 76°C. The scheme provides heat for **over 1000 homes** as well as the Southampton Civic Centre, a shopping centre and the Solent University.

The hot water also generates electricity. By 2007, the system had 11 km of pipes, and was producing 40GWh of heat, 22GWh of electricity and 8GWh of cooling per year.

Energy in the UK is affected by a number of factors and requires careful management and consideration of future supplies.

Are there local projects for a sustainable future?

fig.248 **A new lease of life for farmland by a motorway**

fig.249 **Tides into electricity in Northern Ireland**

Solar power on low-value farmland

Bent Spur Solar farm, near Bolton, has **20,100 solar panels giving a combined installed capacity of 5MW.** This is enough to power around 1,200 homes. The solar farm was built on land adjacent to the M61 motorway on land that had previously been part of a golf course. The panels, while covering an area of 19 football pitches, are just 2.5 metres from the ground and so have a very low visual impact. **Sheep can still graze the grass underneath.**

The farm land is not suitable for crops as it was ruined by spoils after the construction of the motorway many decades ago. It is estimated that this one solar farm would result in a reduction of carbon dioxide emissions by around 1,500 tonnes per year. **The project has permission to operate for 25 years.**

Turning the tides into electricty

SeaGen is the world's largest tidal stream generator and is located at the mouth to Strangford Lough in Northern Ireland. The tides here are some of the fastest and strongest on the planet. Electricity is generated by the tides entering and leaving the Strangford Narrows. SeaGen can generate electricity for between 18 and 20 hours each day. **SeaGen began operation in 2008 and can produce 1.2 MW of power.**

There is also a project to build arrays of tidal turbines between the Scottish islands of **Islay and Jura.** Another project is taking shape in the Pentland Firth. The MeyGen project will construct arrays on the seabed between Orkney and mainland Scotland, eventually generating 398MW. It is estimated that **tides in the Pentland Firth could generate 8% of total UK.**

fig.250 **The Afon Ogwen can provide power for 100 homes.**

fig.251 **Manchester's sewage converted to biogas**

Small-scale hydroelectric projects

The **Ynni Ogwen hydro-scheme** is a small scale hydro-scheme to generate up to **100kW from the water flowing in the Afon Ogwen.** The scheme takes water from the river at an intake weir **upstream of the town of Bethesda.** The water then travels 380m in a buried pipe to a turbine house before being returned to the river.

The low environmental impact of the scheme helped gain local public support. The scheme planned to raise £160,000 from local people to invest in the project though a community share scheme. The share offer was overwhelmingly successful with £459,600 raised in just two months. Construction started in 2016 and was completed in early 2017. **Ynni Ogwen could provide up to 500,000 kWh each year to the National Grid.**

Biogas and electricty from sewage

The Waste Water Treatment Works at Davyhulme, Manchester has been described as **"the most innovative green energy scheme in the world".** The sewage from 1.2 million people is treated at the plant leaving behind a thick black sludge. **This sludge is used to produce biogas (methane) by a process called anaerobic digestion.**

The biogas is used on site to generate electricity as well the heat needed to sterilise the sewage. This reduces the running costs of the plant. **The unused gas not used on site is cleaned and then fed directly into the national gas grid.**

UK biogas is expanding with plants using farm and food waste, as well as sewage. 2016 saw 50 plants adding methane directly to the national grid and more generating electricity.

84

Energy in the UK is affected by a number of factors and requires careful management and consideration of future supplies.

What factors might affect future energy supply?

Future energy supply in the UK will be determined by a range of different factors. The exact balance between these factors is **hard to predict**. It is impossible to know the impact of new inventions, unforeseen economic crises or environmental disasters.

The German government's decision to phase out all nuclear power would not have happened without the unforeseen disaster at the **Fukushima Nuclear reactor in the aftermath of the 2011 Sendai earthquake.**

Technological advances are also unpredictable. **Will a third generation of solar photo-voltaic cells make solar vastly more efficient?** Will large scale storage of renewable electricity, in batteries or as hydrogen gas, make the storage questions a problem of the past? **Would the successful development of nuclear fusion reactors change the energy market forever?**

The boxes below show some of the most important factors which might influence future energy policy in the UK.

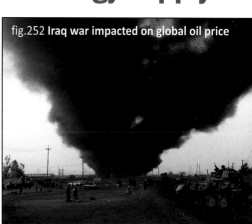
fig.252 **Iraq war impacted on global oil price**

ECONOMIC

⊙ **Large scale power stations are expensive to build.** This was behind the so-called 'Dash-for-gas' in the 1990s, as smaller gas-fired power stations were cheaper to build.

⊙ The cost of **decommissioning nuclear stations** may become so expensive that no company or government will commit to such a future cost.

⊙ **Increasing fossil fuel prices**, caused by a growing scarcity or events such as a Middle East war, could push up the costs. **Renewables may appear a cheaper option.**

⊙ Declining North Sea reserves may make further extraction **too expensive.**

⊙ **Buying cheaper 'fracked' shale gas from the US may be cheaper** than extracting North Sea reserves.

⊙ The **continued reduction in the cost of renewables** may encourage further investment.

▼ fig.253 **Nuclear power remains controversial**

POLITICAL

⊙ **Opposition to fracking could become a significant political problem.** A change in government could see a change in the current pro-fracking policies.

⊙ **Political opposition to nuclear power could see future power stations scrapped.** Many people object to paying extra money to French and Chinese government-owned companies to generate our electricity.

⊙ **Changes to subsidies for renewables can change the economics.** The wind and solar energy industries were kick-started with generou subsidies. These have now been reduced but could be renewed with a change of government.

⊙ **Imports of natural gas, especially from Russia, could become unreliable.** Russia and the West's political disputes could impact on oil and gas prices.

⊙ **Public concern about climate change may force governments to do more to tackle fossil fuel use.**

⊙ Changes to the way public transport is run could either reduce or increase car use.

⊙ Housing regulations could force all new buildings to be **fitted with solar panels and be fully insulated.** This would reduce energy use.

ENVIRONMENTAL

⊙ The need to **meet international obligations** over carbon emissions will mean the government must take action to reduce fossil fuel use.

⊙ **Unforeseen environmental impacts** of fracking may force a change in government policy.

⊙ **Another nuclear disaster, especially if in Western Europe, could force governments to change nuclear policy** and close down reactors which are already past their original lifespan.

⊙ **Opposition to wind farms may stop further expansion on scenic land.** However, s people get used to turbines, public opposition may soften.

⊙ Environmental disasters, such as the BP Deep Water Horizon spill in 2010, may **force stricter rules on exploitation of fossil fuels.**

▼ fig.254 **Deep Water Horizon fire, 2010**

Energy in the UK is affected by a number of factors and requires careful management and consideration of future supplies.

How might energy policy change in the future?

Any predictions about the future of energy in the UK must take into consideration all the possible economic, political and technological issues associated with each source of energy. Environmental concerns may force the energy mix in one direction, while economic issues may act in a different way.

Ultimately, the energy mix in Britain is determined by both **economic factors** (the cost of each energy source) and **political factors**. Different political parties have very different views about business, climate change and the energy mix.

A change in European Union policy allowed the so-called 'Dash for Gas' to occur in the 1990s. **With Britain leaving the EU, further changes in energy policy may well be driven by changes brought about by UK elections**, as well as the actions of businesses, energy consumers and environmental campaigners.

A change in government in Britain could result in changes in energy policy.

This happened after 2010 when the new government started reducing subsidies for solar and onshore wind, while increasing incentives for building nuclear power stations.

Another change in government could see renewables back in fashion, a halt to fracking and, perhaps, an end to the new nuclear programme. **Cheap overseas gas has resulted in its increased use in Britain**. A rise in the wholesale price of gas could result in a reduced reliance on this fossil fuel, especially if prices soar.

Unforeseen events can also change policy or affect energy supply. Civil war in Libya between 2011 and 2015 affected oil production in the Libyan desert. **Production of 1.6 million barrels a day was reduced to almost zero in 2012.** There have been wild fluctuations in production since. This has impacted on the world price of oil and that paid by motorists.

Political conflict with Russia could affect gas supplies. Another nuclear accident, or a delay or problem in

fig.255 Anaerobic digester on Hertfordshire farm

developing new reactor technology, **could delay new nuclear power stations.**

New inventions could significantly reduce the cost of solar compared to gas. New electricity storage solutions could transform the energy market.

The ***Anaerobic Digestion and Biogas Association*** have suggested that biogas from sewage, farm, food industry and household waste could meet 30% of the UK gas needs. To do this would require government support for investment, albeit at a much smaller scale and on a shorter timescale than that agreed to support nuclear power at Hinkley C.

Today some countries are embracing biogas. Oslo's entire bus fleet is powered by biomethane produced from

Thinking it through

1. With reference to fig.245, suggest reasons why the **use of natural gas** has made the UK energy mix **'less secure'** in recent years. (3)

2. What is **geothermal** energy? (1)

3. What is **biogas** and why is it considered to be renewable? (2)

4. With reference to examples, describe ways that Britain could **expand its use of renewable energy.** (4)

5. **"The UK could be a world leader in renewable energy."** Discuss this view. (6)

6. **"Local solutions to energy supply must play an important part** in the UK energy mix." Discuss this view with reference to examples of local solutions. (8)

7. Why is **transport** such an important issue when discussing the **energy mix** between renewable and non-renewable energy in the UK? (4)

8. Discuss the **economic, political and environmental factors** that could change the use and supply of energy in the UK in the future. (12)

Your Revision checklist

For the last unit on the UK you need to know how **air masses, the North Atlantic Drift and continentality** influence the weather in the UK. This must include how air masses cause **extreme weather** conditions in the UK, including extremes of **wind, temperature and precipitation** (pages 63-65).

You need to study a **case study of one UK flood event** caused by extreme weather conditions. This book covers the **Cumbrian floods of 2015**. You must remember the causes of the flood event, including the **extreme weather conditions** which led to the event. You should remember some of the **effects of the flood** event on people and the environment plus the **management of the flood event** at a variety of scales (pages 66-67).

Following from floods, you must have an **overview of how environments and ecosystems in the UK are used** and modified by humans (pages 69-73) This must include the **mechanisation of**

farming and **commercial fishing** to provide food. You should also be aware of **how wind farms and fracking** provide energy and impact on the environment. You should also be aware of a **reservoir** and a **water transfer scheme.**

When studying energy you should Identify both **renewable and non-renewable energy sources** and how they contribute to energy supply in the UK (pages 74-77).

You must study the **changing patterns of energy supply and demand** in the UK (pages 78-86). An awareness of how changes have been influenced by **government decision making** and international organisations is also important. You should be aware of **strategies for sustainable use** and management of energy at **a local and UK level** and whether these have been successful.

Finally, you should be confident to discuss the **development of renewable energy in the UK** and the impacts on people and the environment.

Energy in the UK is affected by a number of factors and requires careful management and consideration of future supplies.